THE HISTORY OF
GUNS

Michelle Brachet

THE HISTORY OF
GUNS

First published in the UK in 2014

© Demand Media Limited 2014

www.demand-media.co.uk

Printed and bound in Europe

ISBN 978-1-910270-79-0

Contents

Introduction

Weapons - as a generic term - have been used since the beginning of civilisation. Primitive designs used for hunting animals led to weapons that were used for defence and warfare. Before guns came bows, spears, crossbows, hand axes, clubs, swords, daggers and many other implements, designed with the sole purpose of inflicting terminal injury on the unfortunate recipient.

Exactly where and exactly when gunpowder was invented is a matter of historical debate. There are several candidates including China, Arabia, Europe and India, although it is generally agreed that the period of invention was during the 13th century or perhaps a little earlier. The discovery of gunpowder (a mixture of saltpetre, charcoal and sulphur) naturally led to the devel-

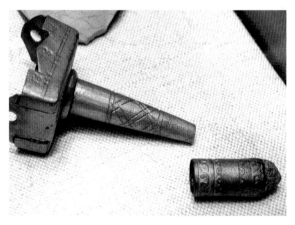

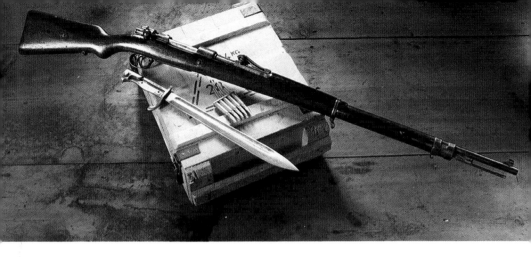

opment of firearms, and weapons that used gunpowder made their presence felt from the 15th century onwards.

A little more certainty can be placed on when the very first gun was invented, which is thought to be before 1326 according to sources. Historically, references to guns become much more common in the years following this. Most likely requiring four hands to fire it, this first design consisted of a simple tube, blocked off at one end but with a drilled hole at that end to allow the gunpowder to be loaded (with the aid of a pole that was also fitted at the breech) ready to be ignited by a hot coal or wire.

The history of the development of guns throughout the centuries is intrinsically linked to historical military events, from the Fall of Constantinople in 1453, the Battle of Pavia in 1525, the French Revolution in 1789, the American Civil War in 1861 to World War I and World War II in the 20th century, taking us to the requirements and developments that warfare in the modern world dictates today. The impact that guns have had on world history is most certainly profound.

With regard to guns for non-military purposes, again social convention and traditions have also had an effect on

LEFT Fitting of a gun powder bottle found 1981 in the wreck of a sunken sailing boat of the 17th century in river Elbe, Germany

their development, as the necessity to hunt for food changed to hunting as a sport, and of course now we have the modern day sports of rifle shooting, competition target shooting, clay pigeon shooting and the like. Guns created and developed for both self-defence and law enforcement is also part of the story here, with the right to carry arms often directly connected to civic rights and social status too in many societies. Although a highly controversial subject today, the right to carry arms

in the United States, for example, is enshrined in the Second Amendment to the Constitution of the country.

There is absolutely no doubt that the emergence of guns had an immediate impact on military warfare, although historians debate whether a 'military revolution' occurred during the first half of the 17th century. What is agreed on, however, is that the development of guns was very rapid indeed; the time separating the earliest flintlock to the modern assault rifle is not even two centuries. With these fast-moving advancements came the ability to create mass armies with fearsome firepower for the very first time. As with all technological and mechanical advancements of the past 150 years or so, the impact that the ability to mass-produce guns had on military history and its future cannot be emphasised enough.

BELOW World War II Infantryman, kneeling in front of M3 Half-track, holds and sights an M1 Garand rifle. Fort Knox, Kentucky, June 1942

Guns fall into various different categories, most of which will be familiar, such as handguns, rifles, machine guns etc. It is probably needless to say that over the centuries the number of different guns designed under each category is vast, and of course this is further amplified by the fact that each continent and each country within developed their own guns in their own way. Quite surprisingly however, there are actually many similarities between weapons of completely different cultures during the same periods in history.

Not only can we now look at the guns of the past, but also in the 21st century, the tremendous variety of models and mechanisms is staggering. It is not possible to document every model of every gun through history to date here, and there are several good published sources that look at this in detail. Here, the intention is to focus on the historical development of general categories of guns set in a chronological context.

Although this book is about the history of guns, it is also important to remember

that other related topics, such as swords and armour, are also an important part of the bigger picture with regard to the history of weaponry as a whole. Just because guns were invented didn't mean that other types of weaponry became defunct, as can clearly be shown by the fact that bayonets were attached to assault rifles by the British Army in the Falklands War and as recently as the War in Iraq.

ABOVE A Soldier test a high tech XM-25 weapon system at Aberdeen Test Center, Md. It features an array of sights, sensors and lasers housed in a Target Acquisition Fire Control unit on top, an oversized magazine behind the trigger mechanism, and a short, ominous barrel wrapped by a recoil dampening sleeve

Chapter 1

The Early Days

Guns spread rapidly throughout the 16th and 17th centuries both in Europe and further afield. The combined effect of the growth of states capable of generating money through taxation and the changes in military and political strategies to adapt to the ever-evolving new firearm technologies meant that both the armies that were sent to battle plus the weapons that were at their disposal became evermore lethal.

The first conflicts to witness the effectiveness of large-scale use of field artillery and firearms on the battlefield were the Italian Wars of 1494 to 1559. It was during this period in history that open warfare was replaced by a long period when siege tactics became the most prominent feature of battle. The arrival of the musket also greatly enhanced these siege tactics.

The Protestant Reformation in the early 16th century had also added a new religious and ideological dimension to warfare that had hitherto been mostly concerned with dynastic issues. By the mid-16th century the battles were becoming bloodier and the armies were getting bigger, causing ever-increasing pressure on those in power throughout Europe.

Traditional battlefield formation was

also affected by the use of firepower. Whereas previously the block formation was used, during the 16th and 17th centuries this gradually changed to line formation. This, however, required greater discipline in the ranks than had previously been necessary, hence the onset of firearm drills which were implemented both for safety and effec-tiveness of firepower. The 16th century also saw Europe flex its military biceps abroad for the first time.

The early 17th century, and notably during The Thirty Years' War of 1618 to 1648, witnessed the growing sophis-tication of both armies and military tactics. For the first time armies started

wearing identifying solid colours, which of course would later become identical military uniforms. This period also saw the change from armies being made up of voluntary mercenaries that would have been disbanded after a particular military campaign, to the formation of established permanent military personnel. By the end of the century, France's army for example, stood at some 400,000. Also in place by the turn of the century was the combination of musket and bayonet.

The constantly evolving firearms and ammunition meant that by the mid-18th century pre-packaged cartridges with the pre-measured charge, combined with the development of the flintlock musket, increased the rate of fire possible by twofold.

With the Seven Years' War that raged from 1754/56 to 1763, the world had endured its very first truly global conflict by the end of the 18th century.

Chapter 2

The Matchlock

The first improvement to the very simple original gun design (as described in the introduction) was the matchlock. The advantages of this design were threefold: it could be fired by one man only; it was for the first time possible to keep both hands on the gun whilst firing; and therefore it was possible to also keep the target in sight at all times.

Typical of a classic European matchlock, the new design was facilitated by the fact that a lock was invented that held a burning slow match (a slow-burning twine or chord fuse treated with saltpetre to keep it alight). Due to its S-shape, this was called the serpentine

lock. Positioned like a pivot at the gun's centre point, the lower arm would be pulled backwards (as a lever in the early designs, which was later replaced with the addition of a spring-loaded trigger) thus pushing the upper arm forwards, allowing the glowing slow match to touch the priming powder in the flash pan. This would have been positioned outside of the barrel but was connected to the main charge of powder and ball by a touch-hole. The serpentine could be positioned either behind or in front of the flash pan, although the latter matchlock design was more common.

In Europe, the matchlock was in use from the mid-15th century onwards and

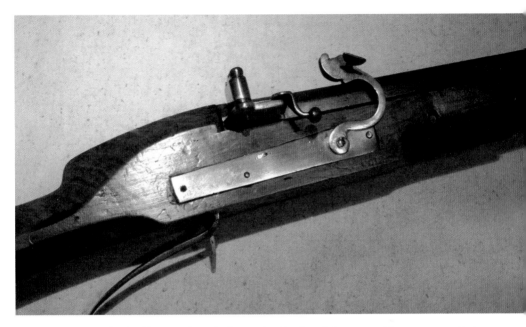

by the 16th century they had become the weapons of choice. Although technically they were superseded by the wheellock design in the 16th century, the fact that the matchlock was such a simple design meant that they were widely used until the end of the 17th century.

A variant design called the snap match-lock was also developed. It was used in Europe from about 1475 to 1640 and in Japan from 1543 to around 1880. This model introduced a weak spring that held the serpentine in firing position, which would be released by pulling a trigger or short string. Unfortunately this model did not prove to be popular with soldiers due to the fact that the

aggressive action of the design often extinguished the slow match before it could ignite the priming powder.

Despite several improvements to the matchlock's designs over the years, the fact remained that it was unpredictable, not to mention cumbersome. One of the most significant weaknesses of its design was the fact that the slow match had to be kept alight all the time, otherwise the gun could not be fired as and when required. The safety issues of a constantly burning slow match when dealing with loose gunpowder was a serious problem, not to mention the difficulty in keeping the slow match constantly burning. In addition to this, the smell and the sight of the glowing slow match at night easily gave away a musketeer's position in hiding to the enemy.

The Wheellock

A far more reliable albeit more complicated gun design than the matchlock was that of the wheellock, invented around 1500 in Europe. Some scholars believe that Leonardo da Vinci was the mastermind behind the design, although this is not comprehensively acknowledged, as other historians believe that the evidence of creation points to an unnamed German mechanic.

The new firing mechanism on the wheellock meant that for the first time gunpowder could be ignited mechanically. A gun with a highly complex

mechanism meant that a very skilled gunsmith was the only person who could make such a weapon and they were therefore also very expensive.

The firing mechanism consists of several components: the 'dog', the wheel, the pan, and the sear or trigger mechanism. The basic functionality of the mechanism works thus: a piece of pyrite is clamped on a spring-loaded arm (the 'dog') that rests on the cover of the pan. By pulling the trigger, a steel wheel (also spring-loaded) spins against the pyrite generating sparks. At the same time the

trigger is pulled initiating the spinning wheel, the pan cover also opens automatically. The white-hot sparks from the pyrite ignite the gunpowder in the pan. This then flashes through a small touch-hole, which in turn ignites the main charge in the gun's barrel and the gun discharges.

Not only did this firing mechanism mean that the weapon was ready to fire in an instant, it meant that it was possible for the first time to fire the weapon with one hand, leaving the other one free. Compared with the earlier matchlock,

ABOVE Double-barrelled Wheellock Pistol of Emperor Charles V, ca. 1540–1545. The Metropolitan Museum of Art, New York

THE WHEELLOCK

BELOW Wheellock mechanism explained

RIGHT Antique pre-Napoleonic Wheellock firearms

other advantages in design and usage included its increased reliability and ease of use in damp or wet weather conditions. The priming pan on the wheellock also had the addition of a cover that didn't open until the instant the gun was fired; this naturally was also advantageous in adverse weather conditions.

Without the need for a constantly lit glowing and odorous slow match, the wheellock was instantly more safe, less obvious to the enemy and could also be concealed under clothing for the first time. Before the introduction of the wheellock, pistols were a rarity and it certainly would not have been possible to holster or pocket a matchlock.

Until the late 16th century, wheellock pistols were known as 'dags' in northern Europe. In order to make it easier to pull the pistol from a pocket for example, these dags were often designed with a round ball-like pommel at the end of the butt.

Several factors led to the wheellock being replaced by a less complicated design called the snaphance or snaphaunce by about 1650. The wheellock was not only more complex and therefore expensive, but it was also prone to breaking, often only repairable if returned to the original maker. It is perhaps not surprising therefore that they were also not mass-produced for military use.

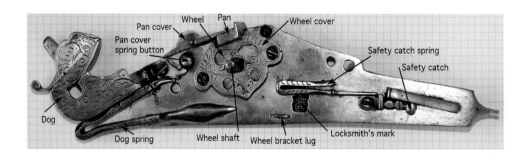

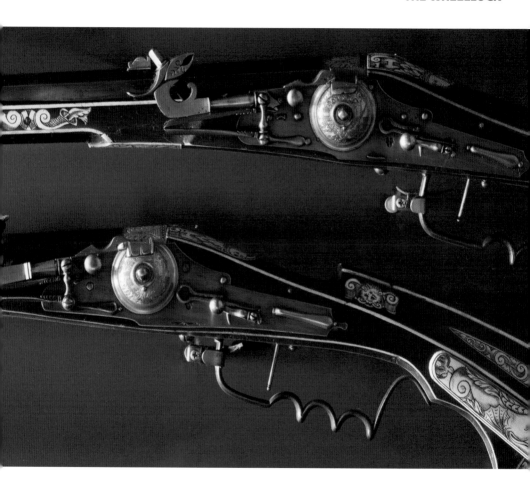

Chapter 4

The Snaphance

The snaphance or snaphaunce is a mechanical progression of the wheellock firing mechanism and basic snaplock firing mechanism, and is the predecessor to the flintlock. Snaplock is the specific term used to describe the particular type of mechanism where sparks are produced by a spring-powered cock that strikes a flint down onto steel to ignite the gun's priming powder.

The name snaphance originated from the Dutch phrase *schnapp hahn* or 'pecking hen' - which incidentally described the action that became known, as it is today, as the 'cock'.

The new design first appeared in the late 1550s and by about 1650 the snaphance had replaced the wheellock firing mechanism and variations of the model were prevalent throughout Europe and North Africa, as well as the Middle East.

It remained popular until around the end of the 17th century, apart from in Northern Italy, where it remained in use until the middle of the 18th century.

The firing mechanism works as thus:

ABOVE A snaphance lock, fired, showing the internal mechanism

unlike the wheellock, the snaphance uses a spring-loaded flint that is held in a clamp at the end of the bent lever, or the 'cock'. As the trigger is pulled the flint strikes a curved plate of hardened steel – known as 'frizzen' in old-English

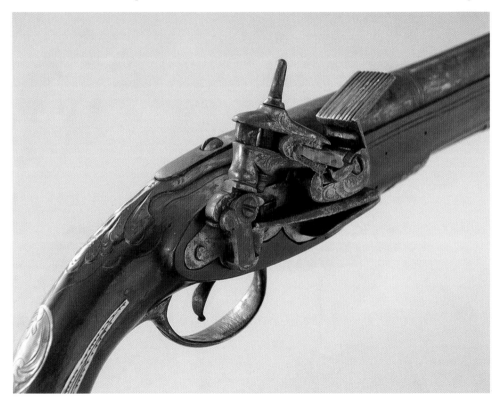

terms, or battery - which in turn creates the hot white sparks to ignite the gun's priming powder.

The snaphance is a more sophisticated version of the snaplock with the main difference being that it has a pan cover that opens automatically, unlike the earlier matchlock and snaplocks, which required the pan to be manually opened. One of the other main advantages of using flint to ignite the priming powder rather than pyrites is that the flint lasted longer.

Until the creation of the Spanish miquelet lock, the snaphance had one particular issue with regard to how the pan cover displaced and this was caused by the awkward way in which it was linked to the trigger.

The miquelet lock was also designed at the same time the snaphance was 'the gun of the day' and is a distinctive version of the former. The miquelet lock was particularly popular throughout Portugal, Italy, Spain and its colonies, North Africa, the Balkans and the Ottoman Empire; its popularity lasted from the late 16th to the middle of the 19th century.

Turning out to be not only the precursor, but also the final technological link that eventually led to the development of the 'true' flintlock mechanism, two predominant forms of the miquelet lock were developed: the Spanish lock and the Italian lock.

Although both the Spanish and Italian locks had their identifying and specific nuances in terms of design, the main differentiating features of the miquelet lock were to do with the horizontal rather than vertical sears (the catch in a gunlock mechanism that holds the cock or hammer at half or full cock and is released by the trigger). This feature is generally accepted to be the defining one of the miquelet lock. This also solved the pan cover displacement issue that the snaphance suffered from. The Spanish rectified this problem with the miquelet lock by extending the foot of the steel and making it the pan cover. At the crucial moment the exposed mainspring would move the pan cover out of the way.

LEFT Spanish Miquelet Pistol

Chapter 5

The Flintlock

RIGHT Examples of
the flintlock firing
mechanism

The flintlock design was perfected by around 1750 and encompasses numerous types of small arms including the musket, pistol, rifle, as well as multi-shot guns. The French gun maker, Marin le Bourgeoys, created the first true flintlock around 1610. [1] He did this by combining the internal mainspring of the snaphance with the single-piece steel and pan cover from the miquelet lock design.

The concept was gradually perfected so that just over a century later the flintlock also encompassed roller bearings that acted on the bridles and springs, ensuring that all of the components of the firing mechanism where kept in perfect alignment at all times; this was the very first time this had been achieved in the history of guns. Although the match-lock, wheellock, snaphance and mique-

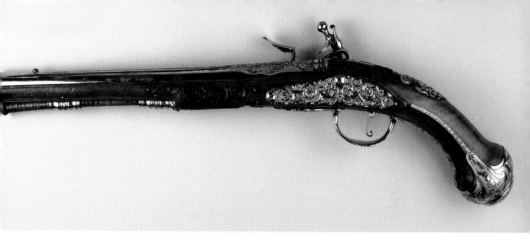

let lock continued to be made for many years following the perfected flintlock, the improvements that the flintlock gave rendered all of these earlier gun models technically obsolete.

Used as both a military sidearm and weapon of self-defence the flintlock pistols in use were mostly smoothbore (i.e. the barrel didn't have helical grooves known as rifling), although some rifling pistols were, however, also produced. In view of the fact that the range of

flintlock pistols was relatively short, they were used militarily in conjunction with other weapons such as the sword.

Made in many different sizes and styles – coat pistol, belt pistol, coach pistol, horse pistol etc. - the main common development of the flintlock pistol is that it gradually reduced in size over the years. By the end of the 18th century the longest pistol would have been about 40cm. The examples of styles named above gives a pretty good clue as to how

ABOVE This pair of Flintlock pistols bears the arms of the young Johan Willem Friso (1687-1711), prince of Orange

---

[1] *Technically speaking, any firearm that used flint to ignite the priming powder can be referred to as a flintlock. To avoid ambiguity here, however, the term flintlock has only been used when talking about the guns that incorporate the specific firing mechanism that Marin le Bourgeoys invented in 1610, which was further developed over the following 200 years.*

these different styles and sizes were used for particular purposes. The smallest pistol would fit into a pocket for men or hand muff for women, whereas the larger coach pistol would have been kept under the seat of a coach. Made in various different sizes, one of the most elegant flintlock pistol designs was the Queen Anne pistol, which became fashionable in England during the brief reign of Queen Anne between 1702 and 1707.

Made and sold in identical pairs, the single-shot British duelling pistol was the height of flintlock mechanical sophistication. It was about the same size as the horse pistol of the late 18th century (approximately 40cm long), but its reliability and accuracy was renowned. Although not often ornate on the outside, the craftsmanship of the internal mechanisms was of a very high standard.

From around 1660 to 1840 the flintlock musket was the preferred choice of firearm for armies throughout Europe and was also used domestically as a hunting gun.[2] Due to the fact that the flintlock musket normally didn't have a choke (a constriction in the end of the barrel) and was of large calibre, it was usually loaded with a lead ball and had a pretty accurate range of between 75 and 100 metres. For military purposes the charge loaded into the gun was often a combination of a ball mixed with (normally) three large shot; this common load was known as 'buck and ball'. The flintlock muskets for military use were of course also designed so that a bayonet could be attached as well.

Although the majority of flintlock guns were smoothbore, there were some rifled types, but due to the difficulties that resulted from rifling the barrel[3], they had limited use on the battlefield and were primarily used for hunting. Rifling the barrel not only makes the gun more accurate but also gives the weapon a longer range. The problem with using this design for an army was that reloading a rifled muzzle-loading gun with a lead ball took longer than that of a smoothbore. The second issue was that after firing so many shots the barrels were prone to getting blocked up with black powder. It goes without saying that there would have been little time for army infantry to fiddle about cleaning the barrels of their guns when under fire from the enemy! Therefore, the little military use that flintlock rifles did see was mostly concerned with sharpshooting and the like, where accuracy rather than volume of shots was the most important aspect for the job in hand.

In the United States a modified version of the European small game rifle led to the development of the American 'long rifle', also known as the 'Kentucky Rifle' and the 'Pennsylvania Rifle'. These were primarily used for hunting and due to the very long barrel of the gun, not only had an impressive range of around 250 metres, but they were also impressively accurate for this period.

In the Middle East, Central Asia, British India and Afghanistan another variation on the European long flintlock rifle was used, primarily for military purposes

ABOVE A Queen Anne pistol with exceptional silver decoration

[2] *The generic description of a musket is that of a muzzle-loading, smoothbore gun. Muskets were made over the centuries primarily for use by infantry, hence the term 'musketeer'. Muskets were made with all of the different firing mechanisms that developed including the wheellock, snaphaunce, flintlock and caplock.*

[3] *See 'rifling' in the glossary of terms.*

15 seconds to reload, a flintlock design was made that incorporated two, three, four or even more barrels so that multiple shots could be fired. These models were notoriously unreliable and when a multi-barrelled gun is unreliable this usually means that it is potentially very dangerous, not to mention how much they cost to make in the first place. The 'pepperbox revolver'[4] was prone to either exploding in the users hand, or firing off all shots simultaneously.

and was called the 'jezail'. Generally handmade and muzzle-loading, they differed greatly in design because each was individual. Unlike the American long rifle that tended to be of a smaller calibre because of its primary function for hunting, the jezail was of a larger calibre, typically with a very long barrel. Again, because of the military requirements, most jezails would have been smoothbore, although some were rifled, which resulted in exceptional accuracy when combined with the very long length of the barrel.

In view of the fact that the smoothbore muzzle-loading flintlock muskets took even the most experienced user around

The development of the flintlock firing mechanism took the world of guns to a new level, but it is not surprising in a time before the technological advancements that developed in the modern era, that they were not without problems and drawbacks. Misfires, accidental firing, workability in damp weather conditions, inherent dangers working with loose gunpowder and reloading issues when the touch-hole became clogged with residue powder were all problems associated with flintlocks. The biggest problem of all, however, was that the flint had to be kept in precisely the correct shape and position for the gun to fire.

The reason that armies would typically fire rounds in volleys stems from the fact that as a flintlock is fired a shower of sparks spray both from the muzzle and out of the flash pan sideways. One man firing closely next to another could easily ignite the others priming powder, hence firing in volleys was introduced to reduce this risk.

The introduction of the enclosed box lock[5] dating back to 1875 was a significant step forward, but apart from that, only small developments occurred to the flintlock over the following 200 years from its creation. It wasn't until the first glimmers of the percussion cap system was patented in 1807 that the flintlock started to be deemed as out of date, but it declined very slowly in popularity; flintlock weapons remained in common use for both civilians and the military throughout the 19th century.

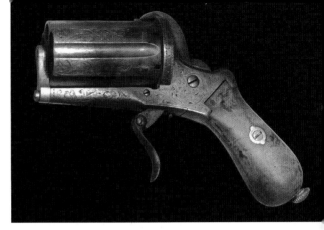

The impact the flintlock had remains very much in evidence today. Such was its longevity and influence that many phrases associated with firearms evolved because of the flintlock: 'flash in the pan', 'going off half-cocked' and 'lock, stock and barrel' for example. Drill commands and positions that are more commonly now only seen during military guard displays also come from the original drills that were devised for carrying, loading and firing the flintlock musket.

ABOVE Example of a Pepperbox revolver

---

[4] *It should be noted that the pepperbox was made with all the different ammunition systems: matchlock, wheellock, flintlock, percussion, pinfire, rimfire and centrefire.*

[5] *A hammerless action commonly used in double-barrelled shotguns that uses hidden self-cocking hammers in a break-open action.*

Chapter 6

Early Hunting Guns

The development of firearms naturally had a direct impact on the landed gentry's hunting habits, both for sporting pleasure and hunting for food. The wheellock, particularly the rifled wheellock, had become a popular gun for these activities by the early 17th century. The rifled wheellock was a hunting all-rounder, even for smaller game such as rabbits.

The only downside to the hunting guns during this period was the length of time it took to reload, in addition to the fact that the gun had to be completely disassembled for cleaning after firing around only 30 rounds of ammunition. There was also a difference in models

of guns made and used for hunting in England compared with those in Europe at this time.

By the start of the 18th century the gap between the English and European gun designs had closed significantly with the flintlock taking precedent in all territories apart from southern Europe. Here the miquelet lock – the more primitive design compared with the flintlock – was still very much in use.

A World of Revolution

From the end of the 18th century through to the beginning of the 20th century, the face of warfare was radically transformed. The political and industrial revolutions that generated rapidly changing new technologies, combined with ever-growing belief systems of nationalism and democracy meant that those in power became more powerful and those who resisted such ideologies were suppressed.

During those 150 years the world endured and witnessed much bloodshed and turmoil. This period in historical warfare included the French Revolutionary and Napoleonic Wars of 1792 to 1815, the first Opium War between Britain and China in 1839, the Crimean War of 1852 to 1855, the

1857 Indian Mutiny against the British, the start of the American Civil War that was fought from 1861 to 1865, the Austro-Prussian War of 1866, the Franco-Prussia War of 1870 to 1871, the 1898 Spanish-American War, and two Boer Wars fought during 1880 to 1881 and 1899 to 1902.

With regard to the development of actual firearms, innovation and invention were the determining characteristics of the 19th century in so many areas of life; gun making was certainly no exception. At the beginning of the century even the most standard and simple design of gun had to be entirely made by hand. Of course this meant that not only were guns expensive to have made, but also to repair if and when they went wrong. With the onset of all the technological and industrial advancements that progressed quickly through the century, the mass-production of guns was seen well before the turn of the century. This not only meant that the cost of guns reduced, therefore making them more accessible to more people, but also the consistency in quality and reliability was for the first time achievable, whereas previously these qualities would have only been found in the most prestigious of guns.

The weaponry used during the two Boer Wars reflected just how much technological advancements had been made towards the latter half of the 19th century and moving into the next. Although more primitive weaponry such as the bayonet was still used, the advent of automatic handguns, smoke-

less gunpowder, machine-fed rifles and machine guns, of course had a profound impact on both conflicts.

Ten years before the turn of the century and the world of guns had seen a century of remarkable advancements in firearms technology. The world's armies were finally using repeater rifles due to the fact that they had at last become reliable and safe enough for general use.

ABOVE Spanish-American War display at Arkansas State University Museum

Chapter 8

The Caplock Mechanism and Percussion Caps

RIGHT Percussion
cap nipple

Although it took a further 20 years following the initial concept of the percussion cap to become a viable and reliable system that would eventually render all earlier ignition systems obsolete, the Reverend Alexander Forsyth developed the rudimentary theory for the system in 1807.

Being a keen wildfowler, the invention came out of necessity – as is so often the case. Forsyth found that the smoke that emanated from the flintlock firing mechanism, as well as the time delay in pulling the trigger and the gun discharging, was enough to scare his prey and evade his shots. Forsyth pat-

ented his system, but in reality, by the time the concept had been developed and refined into a reliable and viable

ABOVE Caplock mechanism

alternative firing system, the patent had run out.

The use of flint was the main source of problem for the flintlock guns and although it was already known at the time that fulminating salts[6] would explode given an impact, they were too volatile to be a serious alternative to flint at the time. In 1800, British chemist Edward Charles Howard synthesised mercury of fulminate by dissolving

ABOVE An Enfield 3 Band Percussion Cap Rifle being fired

mercury in nitric acid and then adding ethanol to the solution. Forsyth then combined this with potassium chlorate[7] and in doing so created a new fulminate-primer that worked perfectly to detonate a gun's charge without a puff of smoke from the primer pan. The gap between the trigger being pulled and the shot exiting the muzzle was also reduced.

Even though the new firing system had been invented to a certain extent, it took nearly another two decades before a successful solution was found to present the fulminate charge to the breech. A solution was developed, however, and that was the 'cap'. The cap consists of two copper-foiled sheets between which the primer of mercuric fulminate sits. Designed to fit over a pierced nipple (also referred to as a 'cone') this is set in place of the touch-hole and is fitted with a tube that goes into the barrel of the gun. A hammer now also replaced the cock and flint.

This new caplock firing mechanism works by pulling the trigger that releases the hammer. When the hammer strikes the cap the mercuric fulminate explodes and forces the nipple to travel down the tube into the barrel where the main powder charge is then ignited and the gun fires.

Altogether, this new firing mechanism was more reliable, quicker and easier to load and more weather resistant than the flintlock. Many of the former single-shot muzzle-loading pistols and rifles were indeed converted. New pistols using this firing system were being made from around 1820. This new firing mechanism was revolutionary compared to what had been, but at a time in history when manufacturing processes were developing rapidly, it only stayed at the forefront of firearm technology for a further 50 years or so. The main issue with all guns to that point in history was the fact that the necessity to load in the muzzle was time consuming. Two developments ensued that would change the nature of guns forever: breech-loading guns and ammunition that integrated the cap, powder and projectile into one single piece of equipment.

---

[6] *Fulminates are chemical compounds that include the fulminate ion. This is a pseudohalic ion, acting like a halogen with its charge and reactivity. Due to the instability of the ion, fulminate salts are friction-sensitive explosives.*

[7] *A compound containing potassium, chlorine and oxygen atoms.*

Chapter 8

Percussion Cap Revolvers

The conversion of existing firearms to the percussion cap system was quickly followed by multiple-barrelled pistols, such as the pepperbox. In this instance, the numerous barrels were mounted on a rotating axial rod so that a new barrel could turn and present itself to the hammer complete with charge and percussion cap.

RIGHT Russian Percussion Caps

In 1836 the young American Samuel Colt invented the very first percussion cap revolver: the Colt Paterson was the very first repeating firearm that had a multi-chamber revolving cylinder and a single barrel. Patented the year before it is thought that the concept for the design of his new cylinder revolver was

inspired by the locking mechanism on a sailing ship's wheel that had a ratchet

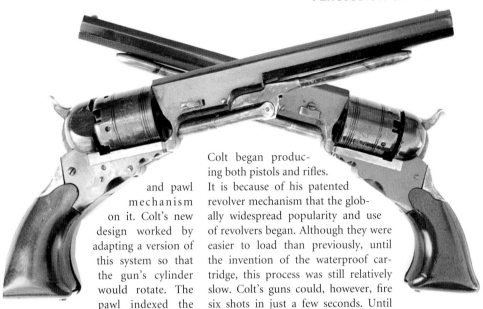

and pawl mechanism on it. Colt's new design worked by adapting a version of this system so that the gun's cylinder would rotate. The pawl indexed the ratchet by one stop every time the hammer was pulled back. Each time this would move a new chamber into line with the barrel and place the percussion cap under the hammer. At the point of firing the cylinder was locked in place by a vertical bolt. The early Colt revolvers were of course single action in design and the hammer had to be manually cocked before each shot was fired.

Colt began producing both pistols and rifles. It is because of his patented revolver mechanism that the globally widespread popularity and use of revolvers began. Although they were easier to load than previously, until the invention of the waterproof cartridge, this process was still relatively slow. Colt's guns could, however, fire six shots in just a few seconds. Until around 1857 Colt really did have a monopoly on the revolver industry and on both sides of the Atlantic.

Colt may have enjoyed the lion's share of the gun market for a while, but the gun makers in London were not sitting on their laurels during this period and revolvers were being made there by the mid-19th century and by, perhaps most notably, British gunsmith Robert Adams.

ABOVE Colt Paterson with loading lever, circa 1839

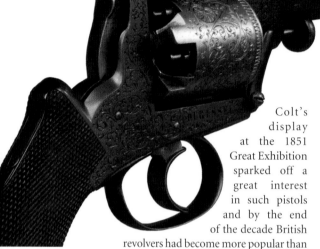

ABOVE Beaumont-Adams Revolver, made by Durussel in Morges circa 1860

Colt's display at the 1851 Great Exhibition sparked off a great interest in such pistols and by the end of the decade British revolvers had become more popular than the American Colts. One revolutionary patent that Adams secured was that of the first successful double-action lock (or self-cocking) revolver. This, in fact, became a lasting characteristic of British revolvers from the very beginning.

The double-action system that Adams had invented meant that instead of having to cock the hammer for each shot, the trigger cocked the gun when pulled. This meant that Adams' revolver could fire much more rapidly than the contemporary American Colt models. The British Army's Small Arms Committee as well as the East India Company approved Adams' revolver.

There were several downsides to this firearm, however. Firstly it was a lot more expensive to produce compared with Colt's mass-produced guns. Secondly, there was a safety issue with regard to powder burns resulting from a black powder 'blowback' due to the fact that the design did not incorporate a recoil shield behind the cylinder. It was also not as accurate as Colt's revolvers because of a longer trigger pull.

A further development and new version of Adams' revolver came in 1855 when, with the help of a Lieutenant Frederick E. B. Beaumont, the trigger was linked to a spurred hammer, which meant that the revolver could be used in single or double-action mode. This new revolver was called the Beaumont-Adams revolver and was extremely popular.

By 1861 Colt's patent had run out and he had to focus on the quality of his guns to compete with all the other manufacturers. At the time, during the American Civil War, the demand for firearms was not surprisingly extremely high. Colt remodelled his .36-calibre Navy revolver that he had designed 10 years earlier to produce the Model 1861 Navy. This streamlined version of the former was produced until 1873 and numbered some 38,843 guns manufactured in total.

BELOW Adams revolver, used by Imperial Russian navy and Finnish customs service. Note the loading lever

Chapter 9

Brass Cartridges

Paper cartridges have been in use for nearly as long as handheld firearms have existed and their use became widespread dating back to the 17th century. Often a cartridge would consist of a paper tube loaded with a charge of gunpowder with a bullet in the end held in by twisting the ends. Often used with muzzle-loading military firearms, the cartridges would have been ripped open by the infantry and the contents poured down the barrel of the gun. These early methods of ignition, as has been discussed above, were replaced by the percussion cap.

Around 1831 a patent had been given for the design of a new type of cartridge. It placed the priming powder in the rim of a cartridge with a thin casing that was coated on all sides with the priming compound.

RIGHT Fired rimfire case (left) and fired centrefire case (right)

Taken a step further and invented by about 1845, the Parisian gun maker Louis Flobert was the first to produce the rimfire cartridge .22BB Cap. These cartridges were very small and initially only designed for indoor target practice; the propellant was fulminate with no gunpowder, as the propulsion came from the priming compound that was distributed just inside the rim. Not surprisingly, the velocity of the cartridge was very low. Not at all dissimilar to a percussion cap, the .22BB Cap had the addition of a round ball pressed in the front, plus a rim to make sure that the cartridge was held securely in the chamber of the gun.

Flobert's cartridges were displayed at the 1851 Great Exhibition and were seen by every prominent gun maker in the world.

Daniel Wesson of American firearms manufacturer Smith & Wesson took Flobert's concept one-step further. The fulminate primer found in the rim of the brass case was combined with both gunpowder and a bullet. In addition to this the rimfire casing was lengthened: the brass cartridge had finally been developed in full. There were two particular problems that gun makers had struggled with for years and this new cartridge solved both: all of the elements required for the gun's ammuni-

ABOVE Box of .41 Short Rimfire ammunition from Navy Arms Company

BRASS CARTRIDGES

tion was now combined into one single item; and the brass casing itself formed a perfect seal at the breech, which guaranteed complete obturation. [8]

With this advancement in ammunition Smith & Wesson produced the first brass cartridge revolver in 1856 after the company secured a deal with the patent holder, Rollin White, who had invented bored-through revolver cylinders.

The company had more than a decade of protected and sole manufacturing of the revolver and its subsequent further developed models. The Smith & Wesson Model 2 was in particular demand during the American Civil War and in 1867 the company went to other parts of the world with their revolvers and ammunition. In particular the Smith & Wesson Model 3 became known as the 'Russian Model'. Not only was this the revolver of choice for the notorious American policeman Wyatt Erp, but the U.S. Army also chose it (known as the 'Scholfield') for the American Indian Wars.

Rimfire cartridges had made a significant contribution to the advancement of firearms, but they were deemed imperfect. By 1866 developments had produced a more robust centrefire cartridge (the primer being in the centre rather than the rim of the cartridge) that was so much better that rimfire cartridges only continued to be used in the very smallest of calibre guns. By the 1860s breech-loading metallic cartridges had made the percussion cap firing system a relic of the past.

By the time that Smith & Wesson's patent ran out around 1869, the improvements in the design of their revolvers had been made so that the cylinder could hold a brass centrefire cartridge. Gun manufacturers all over the world were getting ready to produce revolvers, in what would turn out to be, the final form that the cylinder revolver would historically ever take. As improvements to the design were made over the years, so the speed at which the gun's chamber could be both loaded and emptied increased.

With the later development of self-loading pistols (see chapter on Self-loading Firearms), because of their larger capacity and ease of operation the revolver had been pretty much rendered obsolete by the middle of the 20th century. Thanks to the development of the so-called Magnum rounds that were first designed in 1934, the revolver was, however, given a new lease of life. The reason for this was because the new Magnum ammunition was very powerful; almost twice the energy of a traditional round and the self-loading pistols could not safely handle this new ammunition.

---

[8] *The process by which a gas-tight seal has to be made at the breech.*

Chapter 10

Breech-Loaders

There were many problems asso-ciated with muzzle-loading fire-arms as has been discussed already and by the end of the 18th century many breech-loading systems had been tried without success. The biggest problem was just how to load a gun at the breech and then make a gas-tight seal there (the process of obturation).

The combination of the development of reliable cartridges with a good gas seal was beginning to emerge at the beginning of the 19th century. Throughout the century the development of breech-loading guns ran in parallel with the development of self-contained cartridges.

The 'needle gun' was a turning point for both of the above elements. Developed separately, Swiss gunsmith Jean Samuel Pauly developed the first fully self-contained cartridge in 1808 that was loaded through the breech and fired with a needle; a design that Pauly continued developing. His initial cartridge concept was then improved further in 1836 by the French gunsmith Casimir Lefaucheux.

Johann von Dreyse then created the Dreyse needle gun in 1836, which was the first mass-produced and viable breech-loading gun that facilitated the use of a complete cartridge. The design effectively sealed the chamber by using

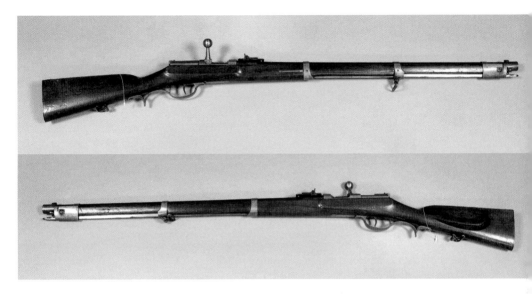

a bolt-action breech-locking system and it fired the self-contained cartridge that had a copper base integrated with the mercury fulminate priming powder and a round bullet that was all encased in paper; the cartridge was fired by a needle. This design was improved over time and it was adopted by Prussia in the 1840s, used in the Austro-Prussian war of 1866 and the Franco-Prussian war of 1870.

Another pioneering bolt-action breech-loading design was invented by Antoine Chassepot. The Chassepot needle gun was used by the French Army in 1867 at the Battle of Mentana; its effectiveness was such that Giuseppe Garibaldi's troops suffered severe losses. A few years later another significant step forward occurred when the rifle was converted so that it was also capable of firing metallic cartridges.

ABOVE Dreyse Needle-gun, 1854, Prussia. From the collections of Armémuseum (Swedish Army Museum), Stockholm.

just the beginning for the company.

One particular type of breech-loading gun that was also successful enough to market, even before the advent of the brass cartridge, was the carbine. Carbines were breech-loaders and were particularly popular for use whilst on horseback as theoretically the guns could be reloaded in the saddle, although this was done very rarely. A longarm[9] weapon, carbines were often just shortened versions of full rifles. They would fire the same ammunition but because of the shorter barrel the velocity of the shot would have been lower. Because of its size the carbine was both easier to handle and lighter, so it made it perfect for use by cavalry. They were, however, less powerful and less accurate than the full-length muskets and later rifles. Of course as the use of cavalry in military history declined so did the use of the carbine. A notable weapon was developed towards

There were many other varieties and solutions tested during this period including the purpose designed Martini-Henry MK1, which was the British Army's first breech-loading rifle. The single-shot breech-loading rifle was arguably, however, perfected by the Mauser brothers. Originally based on the Dreyse needle gun, Paul Mauser developed a rifle that had a turn-bolt mechanism. When the user manipulated the rifle this mechanism cocked the gun. Developments continued until the Prussian government accepted the Mauser rifle in 1871 ... and that was

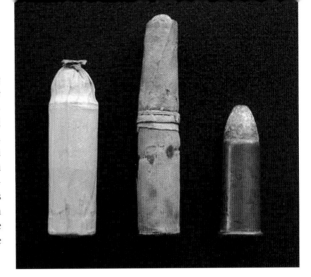

the end of the American Civil War: the Spencer carbine - a shorter and lighter version of the manually operated lever-action Spencer repeating rifle that fed from a tube magazine with cartridges. By the end of the 19th century it was in fact quite common for both full-length bolt-action rifles to be made with carbine versions of the same weapon. This also had the added advantage of both guns using the same ammunition. The Winchester lever-action carbine was one of the most popular and recognisable.

In 1867 John Adams, brother of Robert Adams patented a breech-loading revolver. This was chosen over the Beaumont-Adams as the British government's revolver of choice. Several different models followed, which the British Army and Navy adopted between 1867 and 1880, the most widely used being the last model, the M1872 Mark III. The success of Adams' breech-loading revolvers was such that Adams founded his own company, the Adams Patent Small Arms Company. Until 1880, the John Adams revolver remained the official sidearm of the British Army; the Enfield Mark I replaced it.

By the end of the 19th century most nations had adopted the notion of breech-loading by means of turning a bolt to close, seal and lock the breech. Also by this time, however, the repeater firearm had been developed, not to mention the very early beginnings of the development of automatic firearms.

ABOVE Breech-Loader Cartridges, 1860s

[9] *A longarm weapon is similar to but shorter than a rifle or musket.*

Chapter 11

Repeater Firearms

The definition of a repeater rifle is one that is single-barrelled but contains multiple rounds of ammunition, which are loaded from a magazine either manually or automatically. More often than not, the action that reloads the rifle will also re-cock the firing action. It is also important to note here the difference between what are repeater rifles as opposed to semi-automatic rifles. A semi-automatic system uses the force of one shot to load the next, whereas a repeater rifle following cartridge is loaded by means of a manual action.

Of course, in comparison with the preceding breech-loaded single-shot rifles, the repeater rifles were a significant improvement with regard to the rate of fire that was then possible.

There had been several very early attempts – dating back to as early as the 16th century – to successfully produce manually-loaded repeater rifles and muskets. With all but a few exceptions such as Colt's 'cap-and-ball' revolvers, it was not possible to create a totally satisfactory repeater firearm before the advent of the unitary cartridge that had primer, charge, and projectile all in one package.

By the 1850s breakthroughs were being made with regard to the devel-

opment of repeater rifles and by just past half way through the century they had become commonplace weapons. Now the ammunition was contained in magazines, which as part of one single action, was fed to the breech. However, this single action now also cleared the spent cartridge case from the chamber and cocked the action so that the gun was ready for firing again.

With the success of Smith & Wesson's cartridge revolvers and with the Rollin White patent in place until around 1869, it was just over a decade after the death of Samuel Colt when Colt's Manufacturing Company produced a competitive - and what turned out to be world popular – new bored-through revolver cylinder firearm. The Single Action Army revolver, known as the

ABOVE Mod 1860 Henry rifle, Receiver open, toggle-joint

Peacemaker, was produced in 1873. The gun had a revolving cylinder holding six metallic cartridges and was particularly used at the time by ranchers, outlaws and men concerned with law enforcement. Such was its success that the Peacemaker influenced numerous other gun makers' designs and developments as attempts were made by everyone in the industry to exploit the many advantages of the self-contained brass cartridge for repeating firearms.

Early successful attempts at this were made by two particularly noteworthy individuals: American inventor Christopher Spencer and American gunsmith Benjamin Tyler Henry, who both produced tubular magazine repeater rifles in 1860: the Spencer rifle and the Henry rifle. The magazine could either be placed in the butt or fixed below the barrel of a gun; Spencer's was in the butt and Henry's was below the barrel. A tubular magazine – single

or multiple - was a design in which the cartridges were stored end-to-end inside a spring-loaded tube.

Both of these designs were too imperfect, however, and they did not meet the requirements in order to be commissioned for military use. The biggest problem with both of them was the fact that they could only handle low-powered ammunition. A further generic problem for all who designed guns with them was the tubular magazine. The most serious and dangerous problem was the fact that the tip of the bullet was always butted up against the primer of the cartridge in front of it. Ending unsurprisingly with catastrophic results, if and when it happened, the tip of the bullet packed as they were could act as a firing pin by accident.

Although several other European gun makers designed tubular magazines for their bolt-action rifles, the concept did not last long before it was replaced with box magazines. Box magazines configure the stored cartridges in a staggered zigzag fashion. The implementation of the box magazine was pretty much

the final significant development that this genre of firearms saw. Although further tweaks to designs were made following the box magazine, these were mostly concerned with aspects such as reducing manufacturing costs or making them lighter in weight.

Whilst the U.S. Army stuck to its single-shot breech-loading weapons, the Mauser brothers in Europe began designing rifles with rotating bolts, and with great success, particularly with the M/71. First developed in 1836 by Johann von Dreyse for the Dreyse needle gun, the rotating bolt is a method of locking (see 'lock' in Glossary of Terms). The Dreyse, however, locked using the bolt handle rather than lugs on the bolt head.

Chapter 12

More Modern Times

The 19th century may have witnessed the remarkable and rapid advancements and developments of firearms, but the result of which could not be foreseen and would inevitably change the history of military warfare forever. For the very first time, the 20th century would bear witness to the outbreak of wars on a truly global scale.

Armies had become bigger than ever before and were capable of fighting continent-wide campaigns. The catastrophic events of two world wars not only caused casualties on a scale never before seen but also shook the world economically and morally.

The nature of warfare had been changed forever. In addition to the continuing developments of mechanised guns, of course all other types of weapon systems had been and were being developed alongside: tanks, poisonous gas, aircraft and eventually missiles to name a few.

World War II had seen artillery bombardments, the use of poison gas and tanks, as well as the world's very first purely aerial campaign with the Battle of Britain in the summer of 1940. The Korean and Vietnam Wars witnessed strategic bombing on an enormous scale as well as the first large-scale deployment of helicopters for a military operation.

ABOVE WWII anti-tank
gun display, National
Army Museum

RIGHT Nuclear
weapon test Romeo
(yield 11 Mt) on Bikini
Atoll. The test was
part of the Operation
Castle. Romeo was
the first nuclear test
conducted on a barge.
The barge was located
in the Bravo crater

The culmination of this tumultuous and bloody century of course also gave birth to the ultimate weapon of mass destruction that was both essential yet feared by every superpower in the world – the nuclear weapon.

The nature of modern warfare in the Middle East has now meant that western forces have to employ completely different strategies and tactics to combat the ever-growing threat of global terrorism and in particular has to fight very difficult guerrilla warfare tactics. Even in an age when the world's superpowers have unlimited access to the most advanced weapons arsenal - that would have been absolutely unimaginable a century ago - the very nature of growing insurgency movements, religious fanaticism and genocidal civil wars are creating challenges that even the most sophisticated of weapon systems cannot easily quash.

RIGHT The
AH-1 Cobra
weapon system

Chapter 13

The Development of Self-loading Firearms

RIGHT A Winchester
Mod 05 Self Loading
Rifle, dismounted

A self-loading or semi-automatic firearm is one that automatically initiates all of the procedures necessary so that the gun can fire again and again, subject to a magazine or cartridges being present in the weapon's feed device that is. This would typically mean that the design of the gun includes the capability to re-cock the firing mechanism, load a new cartridge into the firing chamber and after firing extract and reject the spent cartridge case from the firing chamber.

Unlike single-action and double-action revolvers for example, whilst every firearm action has to be manually operated before the very first shot, a self-loading firearm eliminates the need for any manual intervention between each shot – until the cartridges run out of course. The difference between this and a fully automatic firearm on the other hand, is that the trigger has to be pulled for each shot that is required, whereas continuous fire comes from an automatic weapon if the trigger is held down.

Unveiled in 1885, the very first self-loading gun design that was deemed to be successful is attributed to the German-born gunsmith Ferdinand von Mannlicher. This first bolt-action rifle design was the Model 85, which was followed by several other innovative

THE DEVELOPMENT OF SELF-LOADING FIREARMS

ABOVE Mannlicher
M1890 rifle, 1889

Mannlicher rifle designs including Models 91, 93 and 95. Although he was predominantly known for his bolt-action rifles, Mannlicher did also produce some semi-automatic pistols including the Steyr Mannlicher M1894 that held five rounds of 6.5mm ammunition and also was the first to use a blow-forward action.[10]

Throughout the latter half of the 19th century one firearms manufacturer in particular, Mauser, had become a dominant force, especially with regard to rifles designed for military purposes. A German arms manufacturer with a line of bolt-action pistols and rifles, Mauser firearms were built for both the German armed forces as well as

---

[10] *Blow forward is where the barrel is virtually the only moving part of the weapon. It is forced forward against a spring by the cartridge pressure and friction of the projectile against the rifling.*

for export under licence to many other countries. The company also went on to dominate the market on a global scale for heavy-calibre sporting rifles too. Such was the influence of Mauser that more often than not their designs were simply copied by other gun makers. One of the only notable exceptions to this was a British company at the Royal Ordnance Factory in Enfield where a significantly different type of bolt-action rifle was produced. Scottish-Canadian and later American weapons designer James Paris Lee (1831-1904) was arguably best known for developing a spring-loaded column-feed magazine system for centrefire cartridge rifles.

The Lee magazine could be reloaded very quickly, either with single cartridges (like a tubular feed magazine) or with a charger of five rounds. This was made possible due to the fact that he developed and fitted the rifle with a charger bridge. If the magazine was detached then the rifle could also be used as a single-shot weapon. This was popular for both training purposes and to keep some control over unpredictable indigenous troops in foreign countries. Another prominent feature of the Lee magazine was the fact that it was adaptable and could therefore be used with different cartridges and bolt systems, regardless of the length of the cartridge or shape of the bullet. The cartridges were stored in the magazine in a column formation, which also meant that the magazine could be easily lengthened to hold more cartridges if required.

The Lee magazine was perhaps a little too early for its time. The concept was that soldiers in combat would be able to carry multiple loaded magazines therefore speeding up reloading times. However, due to the fact that at the time they were expensive to manufacture, many military forces could not endorse such a potentially expendable item. Instead, the military preference was to issue soldiers with either loose cartridges or en bloc charger clips. [11]

---

[11] *A charger clip, also known as a stripper clip is a speed-loader that holds several cartridges together in a single unit for easier loading of a firearm's magazine.*

It was not until later that the true value of Lee's detachable column-fed magazine system was appreciated and it in fact went on to become the preeminent design used for all modern military small arms.

The aforementioned James Paris Lee and also the Austrian engineer and small armaments designer Ferdinand von Mannlicher designed the en bloc charger clip, which was the preferred military choice over the Lee magazine at the time. The design of the en bloc clip meant that both the clip and the cartridges were inserted into a fixed magazine within the rifle as a single unit. As the last round is fired the clip is ejected or falls from the rifle.

With regard to rifles, the Lee Model 1879 was his first successful magazine-fed rifle. It incorporated the Lee spring-loaded column-fed magazine system with a turnbolt action and was regarded as a landmark rifle design. Both the U.S. and Chinese Navy adopted the rifle until it was replaced by two later designs: the Remington-Lee M1885 and the Winchester-Lee or Lee Navy

M1895. Both were also sold commercially as well as to the military.

There were also two other rifle designs that James Paris Lee is most well known for inventing: the Lee-Metford and the Lee-Enfield series of rifles.

The Lee-Metford rifle was in service by the British Army from 1888 to 1926 and replaced the Martini-Henry rifle. Manufactured at the Royal Small Arms Factory (RSAF) in Enfield in the U.K., its final version was a bolt-action service rifle that combined Lee's rear-locking bolt system and ten-round magazine with a seven groove rifled barrel; the barrel was designed by British engineer William Ellis Metford (1824-1899). A vast improvement compared with other designs at the time, Lee's bolt-action mechanism had rear-mounted lugs which meant that the operating handle was over the trigger and within much easier reach of the rifleman. It could therefore be operated with much more ease and speed compared with other contemporary designs. Also characteristic of this rifle was the fact that the bolt only had to travel the same distance as the

length of the cartridge and its rotation was only 60° as opposed to 90°, which was the norm for many other rifles, such as some French and Mauser-style actions.

Offering greater capacity compared with the competing Mannlicher design, Lee also added a detachable box magazine to replace the hitherto usual integral magazines. The biggest problem with the Lee-Metford rifle was, however, that it used black powder-loaded cartridges

ABOVE A Mauser C96 M1916 "Red 9"

of an anachronism. Despite its many advantageous features compared with other rifles of its day, the use of small-calibre smokeless cartridges had become the norm. The reason being that these cartridges had the capability of propelling bullets at a much higher velocity that also didn't produce as much residue or smoke. When the cordite cartridges were eventually produced, it was then discovered that they weren't suitable for use in the Lee-Metford rifle anyway; after less than 5,000 rounds the shallow rifling wore out the barrels and rendered them useless.

The Lee-Enfield bolt-action, magazine-fed, repeater rifle replaced the Lee-Metford and became the main rifle used during the first half of the 20th century by the British and Commonwealth military forces;

due to a delay in developing ammunition that was going to be loaded with a new propellant called cordite.[12] Unfortunately this was somewhat

---

[12] Cordite is a family of smokeless propellants developed and produced in the U.K. from 1889 to replace gunpowder.

the British Army used the rifle as its standard issue from the year of its official adoption in 1895 until 1957. Even though the Lee-Enfield was officially replaced in the U.K. by the L1A1 SLR in 1957, it remained in service until the middle of the 1960s. With some commonwealth countries still using the rifle (the Bangladeshi and Indian Police for example), it has become the longest serving military bolt-action rifle in the history of guns. Whereas the Lee-Metford rifle took its name from the collaboration of two designers, the Lee-Enfield took its second name from the RSAF where it was designed. In many countries the rifle also became known as simply the '303'.

The rifle's main features included a ten-round box magazine and the cartridges – the .303 British cartridges – were manually loaded from the top; either single rounds or five-round chargers could be loaded.

Other gun makers in Europe also developed their own versions of the James Paris Lee designs, perhaps most notably the aforementioned Austro-German Ferdinand von Mannlicher and the Swiss Rudolf Schmidt; smaller armies typically adopted these guns. Driven by Prussian militarism, and particularly in Germany, many companies were entering the field of armaments production. One notable man was German merchant, manufacturer, philanthropist and member of the Reichstag, Ludwig Loewe (1837-1886). Having been a manufacturer of sewing machines, he proceeded to set up a separate armaments company, Ludwig Loewe & Company (also known as Loewe & Company) after an agreement was reached with the German Army in 1872 to produce rifles for them.

In 1896 Ludwig Loewe & Company combined its weapons and ammunition production to form a new united company called Deutsche Waffen und Muntitionsfabrik (DWM). The first workable self-loading pistol – the Borchardt C/93 – was produced by DWM who, having swallowed up Mauser by that time, also made the most of the Mauser C/96 semi-automatic pistol. Austrian designer Georg Johann Luger (1849-1923), whilst working

THE DEVELOPMENT OF SELF-LOADING FIREARMS

for DWM at the time, also produced the famous Luger pistol (also known as the Pistole Parabellum 1908) – a toggle-locked [13] recoil-operated semi-automatic pistol. Influenced and evolving from the Borchardt C/93, the pistol was used by the Germans in both World War I and II. Prior to these innovative firearms, self-loading pistols had often been regarded as unreliable; this was now not the case, although they were still rather unwieldy and also expensive to produce.

American firearms designer John Moses Browning (1855-1926) designed the first pump-action and self-loading shotguns and he first worked for the prominent American maker of repeating firearms, the Winchester Repeating Arms Company to whom he presented many of his firearm designs until he later moved to working with Belgian company Fabrique Nationale d'Herstal after Winchester refused his working terms.

The Browning Auto-5, first manufactured in 1902 by Fabrique Nationale d'Herstal, was the first successful semi-automatic shotgun. The design was based on a long recoil operation, which continued to be a feature of such firearms for the following 50 years and the gun itself remained in production until 1998. Perhaps his most well known creation is the M1911 single-action, semi-automatic, magazine-fed, recoil-operated pistol. It was the standard-issue sidearm for the U.S. armed forces from 1911 to 1985 (quite a feat) and used in World War I, World War II and both the Korean and Vietnam Wars. Such was the success and popularity of Browning's design that –albeit with some developments over the decades – it was only phased out of service in the early 1990s and replaced with the M9 pistol. Some forces even still use the M1911 pistol today.

By the latter half of the 20th century Browning's work in firearm advance-

---

[13] *A toggle-lock action uses a jointed arm to lock, as opposed to the slide actions of almost every other semi-automatic pistol.*

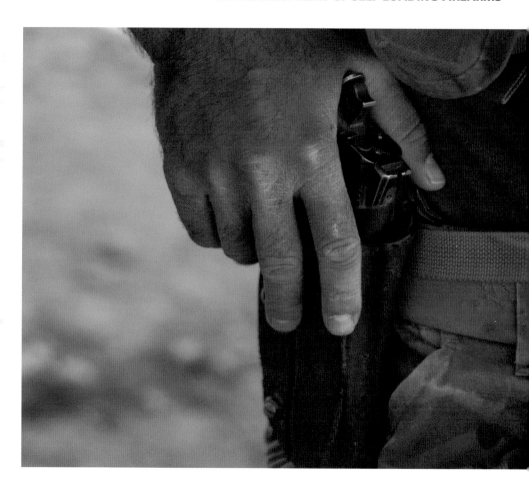

THE DEVELOPMENT OF SELF-LOADING FIREARMS

RIGHT TOP Example of an M1 Garand

RIGHT BOTTOM Clip for an M1 Garand

ments had become a prominent force in the industry. Continuing to work with Belgian firearms manufacturer Fabrique Nationale d'Herstal, the self-loading pistols and later machine gun designs that he was intrinsically involved in developing would become regarded as some of the best firearms in the world for both military and civilian use.

Although Browning had developed the Browning Automatic Rifle in 1918, because of its excessive weight it came to be used as a light machine-gun (see chapter on Machine Guns). A truly practical self-loading rifle was not developed until 1936 when the American M1 Garand was developed and adopted by the U.S. Army; this was the first semi-automatic rifle to be used as a 'general issue' weapon for infantry. General George S. Patton (1885-1945) called the M1 Garand 'the greatest battle implement ever devised' and it remained as the standard U.S. service rifle until 1957 when it was replaced by

the selective fire M14 rifle. [14]

The design of the M1 Garand combined the following features: air-cooled, gas-operated, clip-fed, and semi-automatic – and it was a shoulder weapon. The U.S. military forces used the rifle extensively in World War II and the Korean War. Still used by drill teams and for guards of honour by the military, the M1 is still a sought after rifle for civilians for target shooting, hunting and as a desirable military collectible.

World War II became a catalyst for further developments of the self-loading rifle and one of the best examples of this is the Sturmgewehr G44 German assault rifle, also known as the StG44. 'Sturm', literally 'storm' as in military attack, was the name given to the weapon by Adolf Hitler. This Nazi creation was the first of its kind to be deployed on a vast scale and is regarded by many as the very first example of the modern assault rifle (see chapter on Assault Rifles).

---

[14] *Selective fire is a firearm that has at least one semi-automatic and one automatic mode, which are activated by means of a selector that varies depending on the weapon's design.*

Machine Guns

**The definition of a machine gun
is that of a firearm that is fully
automatic, therefore designed to fire
bullets in rapid succession from a
magazine or ammunition belt, often
with the ability to fire several hundred rounds per minute. There are
also deviants of the true machine gun
including the submachine gun and
assault rifles for example.**

The concept for inventing a rapid-fire
weapon was something that had been
on the minds of inventors since the
early 18th century. Although it was
never taken any further, a London lawyer called James Puckle patented what
he named 'The Puckle Gun' in 1718.

Intended to be used on ships, Puckle's
design was a flintlock revolver cannon
with the capability of firing nine rounds
before it needed reloading. Puckle is
regarded as the first forefather of multi-shot weapons.

Successful machine gun designs did
not, however, come into being until
the early to mid-19th century. The two
key components that were needed to
create a machine gun were the high
fire rate capability and the automated
ammunition loading process. Although
still hand-operated, American inventor Richard Gatling (1818-1903) produced his first workable hand-cranked
multiple-barrel machine gun in 1862,

which is the most well known early rapid-fire weapon and the forerunner of the modern machine gun. For the first time a firearm had been invented that facilitated controlled sequential firing and automatic loading.

The basic operational concept of the first Gatling gun design was based on a cyclic multi-barrel that synchronised the firing and reloading sequence as well as facilitating a cooling process so that the barrel didn't overheat. Cartridges were introduced from a top-mounted hopper into the open breech of the barrel in the twelve o'clock position. The breech closed on its way down to six o'clock and that barrel was fired. It opened again on its way back to the top, ejected the spent cartridge, loaded a new round and cooled down to an extent during that process.

Somewhat ironically perhaps, Gatling invented the gun to try and minimise infantry deaths and to highlight to the world just how very futile the act of war is. In 1877 he wrote, 'It occurred to me that if I could invent a machine – a gun – which could by its rapidity

of fire, enable one man to do as much battle duty as a hundred, that it would, to a large extent supersede the necessity of large armies, and consequently, exposure to battle and disease be greatly diminished.' [15]

The Gatling gun was employed by the Union Forces for combat during the American Civil War in the 1860s and later during the Spanish-American War in 1898; it remained in service until 1911. It may have not been fully automated, but the Gatling gun unarguably represented an enormous development step with regard to firearm technology.

RECOIL AND GAS-OPERATED MACHINE GUNS

Built in London in 1883, American-born inventor Hiram Stevens Maxim produced his machine gun, the Maxim gun; it was the very first true fully automatic weapon in the history of guns.

Maxim's mechanism was based upon using the weapon's recoil to extract a fired case and then chamber another,

ABOVE A model of
a typical entrenched
German machine
gunner in World War
I. He is operating a
Maxim gun, wearing a
Stahlhelm and cuirass
to protect him from
shrapnel

whilst at the same time cocking the action; it was one of the earliest recoil operated firing systems in history. When the trigger was held down, the entire process repeated automatically until the ammunition supply was exhausted, or as happened too frequently in the early days, the gun jammed. With the requirement to manually crank the mechanism now removed, it was greatly more efficient and a lot less labour intensive to operate than the earlier rapid-firing guns.

The Maxim gun was capable of firing at

[15] *Quoted from Paul Wahl and Don Toppel, The Gatling Gun (Arco Publishing, 1971)*

MACHINE GUNS

least 500 rounds per minute, but because the gun still had to be water cooled to prevent the barrel from overheating it was still not that easy to operate it was also heavier and more bulky than the machine guns of the future would be.

One of the main disadvantages of the Maxim gun for military use was that, initially, it gave off a lot of smoke therefore identifying the position of the troops. Of course smokeless propellants had yet to be invented so the idea of using propellant gases to cycle the action was out of the question due to the residue that smokeless powder produced. When the smokeless propellants were developed in the 1890s it changed everything.

It may have taken several years for the real impact of Maxim's invention to be grasped, but when it was, the effect that it, its future variants and its derivatives had on the very nature of warfare in the future was quite profound.

It was not until the 1910s that anyone came close to Maxim's method of harnessing a gun's recoil and the British engineering conglomerate Vickers Limited was the only new design that existed and then it only incorporated small modifications. After purchasing the Maxim company outright in 1896, Vickers took the design of the Maxim gun and improved it. The British Army adopted Vickers MK1 in 1912 as a replacement for the Maxim. The main difference from the Maxim was to do with the reduction in size of the receiver. This was achieved by the fact that its locking toggle-joint[16] broke upwards as opposed to downwards. The rate of fire was around 450 rounds per minute, but the Vickers MK1 was 13.6kg lighter than its predecessor due to the fact that it was made entirely of steel.

By the outbreak of World War I Maxim's original patents had also expired and competing derivative designs from other countries were already in produc-

---

[16] *A toggle joint is a device consisting of two arms pivoted at a common joint and at their outer ends and used to apply pressure by straightening the angle between the two arms.*

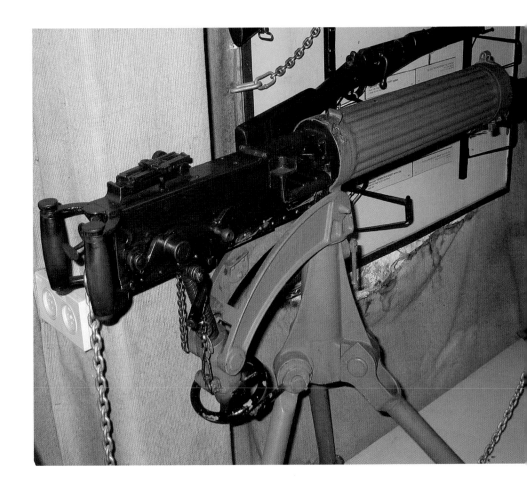

tion. Britain, Germany and the Soviet Union as was, however, not only relied heavily on Maxim's gun designs now developed by Vickers, but they arguably took precedent throughout the war over any other. In fact the British Army were still using the Vickers gun throughout World War II too and the machine gun was only declared obsolete in 1968.

BELOW A Browning M1917 Machine gun, Hackenberg museum

The French on the other hand were developing a gun that also saw the advancement of the gas-operated machine gun. In contrast to the Maxim gun that was recoil-operated and water-cooled, the Hotchkiss machine gun was gas-actuated and air-cooled. Originally the concept was the brainchild of an Austrian cavalryman, Captain Odkolek von Augeza. The French arms company Hotchkiss et Cie based near Paris bought the patents in 1893. The original design had numerous teething problems, particularly its propensity to overheat. It was, however, both robust and simple.

Between 1897 and 1914 the design was refined several times by Hotchkiss armament engineers to correct its inherent faults, but also to make it cheaper to produce and improve its feed mechanism, which used, not fabric belts, but rounds of 24 held in metallic strips.

The Hotchkiss Mle M1914 eventually replaced its predecessor - the St. Ètienne Mle 1907 - and became the machine gun that the French Army used as standard throughout World War I by which time some 47,000 had been produced and issued to them; it remained in service until the early 1940s. One of the most obvious advantages that the Hotchkiss Mle M1914 had over its predecessor was the number of components that it was made from: 32 separate parts as opposed to 64.

The U.S. also used the machine gun during World War I and between 1817 and 1918 purchased some 7,000 for the American Expeditionary Forces (A.E.F.) for front-line offensives.

Another important and contemporary firearms designer whose machine gun designs were both ground-breaking and historically influential at the time was John Moses Browning. He had already developed the Colt-Browning M1895 at the end of the 19th century, which was the first successful gas-operated machine gun to enter service and had refined the short recoil principle with

his already mentioned M1911 pistol. He then went on to develop a new way of harnessing the force of a machine gun's recoil, which was a technical advancement from Maxim's method.

With the heavy machine gun Browning M1917 design, he came up with a simpler method of locking breech-block and barrel compared with what Maxim had done. It was also much lighter than several of its contemporaries, such as the British Vickers machine gun. This belt-fed water-cooled machine gun was adopted by the U.S. armed forces and saw service in World War I, World War II, the Korean War and in Vietnam. Although the Vickers and Hotchkiss machine guns had arguably better weapon systems that had some 50% longer range than the M1917, its rate of fire and solid reliability meant that it was also highly effective in service. The M1917 was used at battalion level, often mounted on top of jeeps and on some aircraft; it had a firing rate of 450 rounds per minute. A variant of the machine gun, the M1917A was then developed and used thereafter. This model had a firing rate of 450 to 600 rounds per minute.

A further variant then saw the M1918 arrive, but too late for World War I. This was an air-cooled version of the M1917 specifically designed for use on aircraft. It had a heavier barrel but lighter barrel jacket than the M1917 and was used by the U.S. until the development of the M1919.

Losing its water jacket, a simplified air-cooled and lighter version of the original M1917 was then developed. This became the .30 calibre medium machine gun M1919 that served alongside the M1917 for many years and remained in service itself in the same form until the 1960s. It was used by the U.S. military and by other countries for a multiple of purposes: as a light infantry weapon; a coaxial gun on tanks; mounted on aircraft; and used as an anti-aircraft machine gun. Although newer machine guns, such as the American General Purpose Machine Gun (GPMG) M60, superseded it by the latter decades of the 20th century, the M1919 and its numerous variants and derivatives continued to be used in many NATO and other countries. By the 1990s the design had been re-chambered for the new NATO 7.62 x 51mm round and it is still in use as such in some countries to the present day.

Although the U.S. Army was happy with the Browning machine guns that were in service, the need for a heavy machine gun became apparent. Starting life in 1929 as the M1921, the water-cooled .50 calibre machine gun was developed until it was replaced in 1933 by the M2 – an air-cooled, belt-fed machine gun that fires from a closed bolt and operates on the short recoil principle of its predecessors. Using the much more powerful .50 BMG (Browning Machine Gun) cartridge meant that the gun had both good long-range accuracy as well as immense stopping power. Like the Browning rifle-calibre gun, by the time the M1921 had metamorphosed into the M2, its water jacket had also been removed.

The Browning M2 has given decades of service to the U.S. military and was used extensively in numerous wars over the century and into the next. It is effective against infantry, light fortifications, vehicles and boats – unarmoured and lightly armoured - and low-flying air-

ABOVE A Browning M2 after firing

craft. From World War II, the Korean and Vietnam Wars to being used in the more recent Iraq and Afghanistan conflicts, the M2 is one of the longest serving small arms in the U.S. weapons inventory. Of course, many NATO and many other countries have also put it into service; the M2 holds the record for being the machine gun with the longest continuous service record in the world.

Finally, the Browning M2 has had numerous different designations over the years, but the current type is the infantry Browning Machine Gun, Cal. .50, M2, HB, Flexible.

During the interwar years the first widely used and successful General Purpose Machine Gun (GPMG) was developed in Germany – well in fact secretly abroad because Germany was officially prohibited from developing new weapons under the Treaty of Versailles. The Maschinengewehr 34 or MG34, followed by a refined and cheaper variant, the Maschinengewehr 42 or MG42 were produced. The MG42 was deemed as the best automatic weapon of its day and was capable of firing 1,200 rounds per minute. It had such a lasting influence that many other modern machine guns – the U.S. M60 and the FN MAG for example – all use certain elements from the original MG42 design. The GPMG that the current German Army uses is the MG3 and this is a direct descendent of the MG42.

BELOW An MG 42 delayed roller locking system

LIGHT MACHINE GUNS

The very first generation of machine guns were very cumbersome, had to be operated by several personnel and were therefore only useable in fixed positions. A requirement therefore very quickly arose for a lighter and more portable weapon that could still produce sustained fire but could be employed by an individual soldier - the light machine gun (LMG).

The first light machine guns were introduced during World War I with the intention of giving extra firepower to the infantry. The U.S. Army and Marine Corps used the Browning Automatic Rifle, which even though was intended to be a self-loading rifle, was also suitable as a light support weapon. Regardless of the fact that it had a fixed barrel and the magazine capacity was not good, the Americans used it on the front-line until the 1950s. Originating in the U.S., the British Army adopted the Lewis gun in 1915, which was an air-cooled, gas-operated light machine gun and kept it as their standard light support weapon

until the Bren Gun superseded it in the late 1930s. The Bren, albeit with various modifications over the years, became the British Army's main light support weapon until the 1990s.

The MG08/15 was Germany's first attempt at a light machine gun and was a modification of the Maxim MG08, but now with a buttstock, a conventional trigger and a pistol grip. Introduced in 1917, it was far too heavy, but all the same it became the main support weapon for the German Stormtroopers and some 130,000 guns were produced.

ABOVE An MG-08/15 machine gun, Batey ha-Osef museum, Tel Aviv, Israel

The problem that many early machine guns had with overheating barrels was no different for the early light machine guns either. As advancements in firearm technology moved forward, however, systems that enabled barrels to be quickly and easily changed, even during combat, eventually solved this problem for good.

One of the most significant differences between the combat fought in World War I as opposed to World War II was that military engagements during the latter were often in situations where shorter-range accuracy and fire was required. This led to two significant changes with regard to the design of light machine guns: the ammunition used became lighter and lower-powered than previously and the barrel of the guns became shorter. Of course this also meant that the total weight of equipment that an individual soldier had to manage was also reduced significantly.

The ammunition feeding systems of the light machine guns also varied to some extent. The Bren Gun and the Browning Automatic Rifle were magazine-fed, whereas others could be fired with a belt or a magazine.

Modern light machine guns have become lighter than ever before, especially since wood was replaced with plastic and since 'bullpup' configurations were introduced (see chapter on Assault Rifles). They also often fire smaller-calibre cartridges and are more compact, with ammunition normally belt-fed from a detachable box magazine. Some light machine guns are also adaptations of existing assault rifle designs, which means that both guns share the same ammunition; the Russian RPK74 is a good example of this. Developed from the successful AKM assault rifle, many of its parts are interchangeable with those of other Kalashnikov-type weapons.

One of the most modern light machine guns that highlights where this genre of firearm is at present is the Heckler & Koch MG4 light machine gun. Initially known as the MG43 the gun was first produced in 2001 and is one of a new range of light support weapons chambered for the standard NATO 5.56mm round. It is a conventional belt-fed, gas-operated light machine gun, although the action is based on a rotating as opposed to roller-locked bolt. With a cyclical rate of 750 rounds per minute it is robust enough to function as a sustained-fire weapon. Its light weight means that it is highly suitable for playing the necessary military roles required of a light machine gun. As with virtually all 21st-century firearms, where possible the use of moulded glass-reinforced polymers is maximised. The MG4 also has an integral bipod as well as

mounting points for an M2 tripod and all standard NATO optical sights can be fitted to it. With a hammer-forged quick-change barrel system, the barrel can be safely changed in seconds and without the need for protective gloves.

Definitively sometimes a little confusing, the difference between what constitutes a light machine gun as opposed to a medium machine gun is also not always just to do with its particular design specifications; its usage can also

be a determining factor. If a GPMG is deployed for the intention of sustaining fire and from a tripod position, then this would be considered a medium machine gun. If, however, a GPMG is deployed with a bipod for firing short bursts from the prone position, it would therefore be considered a light machine gun. Light machine guns can also be fired on the move when suppressive fire is required to neutralise or suppress the enemy, or when cover fire is required in a combat situation.

ABOVE A Spanish Army Heckler & Koch MG-4E

Chapter 15

Submachine Guns

A submachine gun (SMG) is a firearm that combines the automatic fire of a machine gun with the cartridge of a pistol. They are highly effective weapons when it comes to close-quarter combat because the low-powered pistol cartridges – good for short-range targets – makes the gun more controllable in fully automatic fire. Their small size and light weight is quite obviously an advantage in terms of manoeuvrability.

Attempts to produce a light, rapid-fire weapon focused on pistols in the early days. Due to the fact that the first generation of rapid-fire pistols were regarded as particularly cumbersome,

expensive and difficult to control, self-loading pistols may have had their place, certainly during World War I, but in an era where mechanised warfare was developing quickly, the necessity for self-loading pistols to be carried declined significantly. Apart from providing a feeling of security as a personal sidearm, self-loading pistols became less of a military weapon, but were not, however, deemed obsolete; they just found different roles in life. As ever-growing requirements for personal and professional security developed, so did the pistol, but with these specific roles in mind. The disadvantages of the pistol for military use were the precursor to the creation of the submachine

ABOVE A Bergmann
MP18

gun. What was required was a firearm that would be more akin to a carbine, but with the ability to fire the type of reduced-power ammunition that handguns used.

Before World War I attempts had been made at converting stocked pistols from semi to fully-automatic. The Germans, Italians and Americans all worked on developing the ammunition around the time of the war's outbreak and further design developments were concentrated at the latter stages of the war in an attempt to gain advantage in the trenches.

These types of weapons became particularly popular in America during the 1920s and 1930s. The Thompson, com-

monly known as the 'Tommy Gun' was an American submachine gun invented by U.S. Army officer John T. Thompson in 1919. Used by both criminals and law enforcement officers, the Thompson is closely associated with the Prohibition era in American history.

Made in 1918, the very first true submachine gun to be produced and used in combat was the Bergmann MP18, which was employed by the German Army during World War I as the primary weapon in trench combat. Such was the impact that this new weapon and its firepower capabilities had shown during the war, that Germany was banned from continuing development and further production of them under the Treaty of Versailles.

The production of the MP18 ceased in the 1920s, but its design was a major influence on the submachine guns that were developed and produced for the following 40 years. As the submachine gun as a concept was accepted by the military all over the world, during the 1930s many countries developed their own designs including Britain, the Soviet Union and Argentina. Britain adopted the Lanchester submachine gun and it was primarily used by the Royal Navy during World War II.

It was not until the onset of World War II, however, that submachines guns were produced and issued on an enormous scale, yet they were still fairly unsophisticated. Producing both a lot of noise and devastating short-range firepower, they quickly became of reduced military value because they were difficult to control and notoriously inaccurate. It was, however, realised at this time that the buttstock was surplus to requirements and could be eliminated from a weapon's design with no negative consequences. Most small arms engagements happened within about 90 metres and a high rate of fire was more effective than - albeit more accurate - slower fire. These were all very significant realisations following World War II that had an impact

on future military firearm design and development, particularly the assault rifle.

It is also important to note that submachine guns have never been seen as replacements for the infantryman's assault rifle either. In fact quite the reverse is true: the development of submachine guns was an important step in the development of modern assault

ABOVE A Bergmann MP18.1, Loading a Trommel Magazin 08

LEFT A model of the original 1921 Thompson submachine gun with a 20 round magazine clip manufactured by Colt. On display with an original sales poster

rifles. Whilst the submachine gun is currently widely used by both police, specialist units and counter-terrorist forces, it has largely now been replaced by the carbine-length assault rifle with regard to military use.

German small arms manufacturer Heckler & Koch's MP5 is a 9mm submachine gun that was developed in the 1960s. There are now over 100 variants of the original design, including a semi-automatic version, and it is the submachine gun of choice for the majority of police and Special Forces units in the Western world. The MP5 is considerably more accurate and controllable in automatic mode compared with other submachine guns. This is largely due to the fact that the mechanism used is similar to Heckler & Koch's range of assault rifles. It employs a roller-locked delayed-blowback action and also fires from a closed bolt, whereas the bolt is held back when the gun is cocked on most submachine guns.

Often also considered as a submachine gun is the firearm that has since evolved from it: the personal defence weapon (PDW) is a compact semi or fully-automatic gun that fires pistol-calibre cartridges. A hybrid between a submachine gun and a carbine, the PDW is more accurate, has a better range and has armour-penetrating capabilities. It is also small, light and the low recoil enables sharper accuracy.

LEFT Heckler & Koch MP5

BELOW CBJ-MS PDW (swedish personal defence weapon)

Chapter 16

Assault Rifles

The modern definition of assault rifle (and not to be confused with assault gun[17]) is a selective fire rifle that uses an intermediate cartridge and a detachable magazine. There are several design factors that strictly define the characteristics of an assault rifle: it must have a buttstock and therefore be capable of firing from the shoulder; it must have selective fire capabilities; it must use an intermediate cartridge; it must use a detachable magazine as opposed to a feed-belt; and it should have a firing range of at least 300 metres. These technical aspects constitute a true assault rifle, although the term 'assault rifle' is often misused for political or commercial purposes.

Following World War II, the most important development of the assault rifle's design came with the 'intermediate' ammunition round[18](or cartridge). It was following this that the weapon became universally accepted; the development of the assault rifle was therefore driven by ammunition technology.

The problem that had to be solved was that using handgun ammunition in an assault rifle was only effective for short-range use. Conversely, because of significant recoil, full-sized military rifle calibres were not comfortable to fire repeatedly, not to mention the large size meant that the rifles became very heavy and therefore also difficult to control

during fully automatic mode. Naturally, the cost of producing full-size rifle ammunition was also a contributing factor driving the development of a new solution. What was needed was a lighter, more compact selective fire weapon that was capable of firing a cartridge that could combine the power of a rifle and the controllability of a pistol cartridge. The resulting ammunition, the intermediate cartridge, would eventually have the accuracy of the former for typical combat ranges, and the firepower of the latter at short ranges.

ABOVE An Afghanistan National Police (ANP) instructor demonstrates to ANP recruits how to aim an AK-47 rifle at a range near the regional training center for the ANP near Gardez, Afghanistan.

[17] *An assault gun is a gun that is mounted on a motor vehicle or armoured chassis.*

[18] *The intermediate cartridge is less powerful than typical full power battle rifle cartridges but still significantly more powerful than pistol cartridges.*

Although the StG44 is recognised by some as the first assault rifle, there are other contenders, such as the Russian Fedorov Avtomat rifle, which was the first assault rifle to be used in service. In 1947, however, one Soviet creation that used a fully developed intermediate cartridge was produced and made its mark on the world of guns from that year – the AK47 assault rifle: a selective-fire, gas-operated 7.62 x 39mm assault rifle; it was one of the first 2nd generation assault rifle after the German StG44.

Designed by a young Soviet tank commander, Mikhail Kalashnikov, the first AK47 design was simple, it was easy to handle and operated in just about any conditions. The rifle was adopted by the Soviet Army in 1949 and was also used by most of the member states of the Warsaw Pact[19].

There were, however, early production problems with the original AK47 design. The rifle was initially made from pressed metal parts, welded components and stampings, but when difficulties were encountered in welding the guide and ejector rails, rejection rates were high. This was, however, rectified and from 1951 a heavy machined receiver replaced the sheet metal receiver. Although this was costly to do, the rate of production sped up.

With the initial production problems resolved, a redesigned model, the AKM, was introduced to military service in 1959. Lighter than the AK47 the AKM now had strengthening ribs in the top surface of the receiver. It also had a reduced cyclic rate of full automatic fire, which as a result, greatly improved its accuracy. Partly because of the easier production of the stamped receiver, the AKM has been produced in vast quantities; both licensed and unlicensed Kalashnikov weapons produced abroad are in the main the AKM version of the assault rifle.

It is generally thought that the ammunition used for the Kalashnikov assault rifle – the 7.62 x 39mm cartridge – was based on the World War II MP43/MP44 designs.[20] Soviet designers, had at the time however, also been developing their own intermediate cartridge with the initial focus on increasing the com-

---

[19] *The Warsaw Treaty Organisation of Friendship, Cooperation, and Mutual Assistance (1955-1991), also known as the Warsaw Pact was a mutual defense treaty between eight communist states of Central and Eastern Europe.*

[20] *MP43 and MP44 are designations of the StG44, which denote earlier development versions of the same weapon but with some minor differences.*

bat efficiency of their submachine guns.

In 1974 the Soviet Union developed a further refined version of the AK47 and the AKM and produced the AK-74. This assault rifle was designed to use the smaller intermediate cartridge 5.45 x 39mm instead of the original 7.62 x 39mm chambering of the earlier weapons.

Although there have been several improvements in design since the original AK-47, the terminology in the West often refers to any rifle based on the Kalashnikov design as an AK-47. Clearly, this is not technically correct when speaking of later versions of the rifle. In most former Eastern Bloc countries the generic terms 'Kalashnikov' and simply 'AK' are used.

The Kalashnikov rifle has achieved iconic status due to its rugged simplicity. Bearing in mind it was originally designed with arctic Soviet conditions at the forefront of operational concerns, its ruggedness and reliability in adverse conditions has become legendary. Added to the fact that it is fairly compact in size, is easy to clean and maintain and is relatively inexpensive to manufacture on a massive scale, it is perhaps not surprising that Kalashnikov is probably one of the most commonly known names in the world of firearms.

Since its inception more than 60 million Kalashnikov-type rifles and light machine guns have been produced. Now mass-produced on a global scale, they have become the most popular guns in the world.

During the post-World War II era the assault rifle became the standard military rifle, with the Soviets leading the way, it was quickly adopted by other nations and each began developing and refining their own preferred versions. The nature of the combat during World War II had highlighted the fact that the majority of infantry combat occurred between 200-300 metres and that it was the weaponry with the highest rate of fire that became victorious in battle. In view of the fact that the full rifle cartridges were therefore unnecessarily powerful, the benefits of the intermediate cartridge for such warfare was unquestionable: faster firing, more bullets being fired, less recoil and a lighter weight meant that more ammunition could be carried by each soldier. The need for rifles with longer ranges and powerful cartridges had become surplus to requirements with regard to changing modern warfare tactics.

A new type of assault rifle started entering military service around the world during the last quarter of the 20th century. Known as the 'bullpup', the design employed a new configuration in which the action is located in the butt with the magazine behind the trigger. This meant that the overall length of the gun could be reduced, but without reducing the length of the actual barrel, resulting in a further reduction in weight as well as better manoeuvrability, especially in confined spaces and accuracy at range. The concept for the bullpup was actually used in some bolt action and semi-automatic firearms in the first quarter of the 20th century.

Having escaped German and Russian forces Polish engineers made their way to England and became part of a 'Polish

design team' at Enfield Lock's Royal Small Arms Factory. With the influence and inspiration that the StG44 had shown them during the war, work commenced on designing a new rifle that would fire, instead of the .303 cartridge, the optimal .280 inch (7mm) interme-

BELOW A Ukrainian Marine armed with an AKS-74U carbine in a line during civil disturbance operations, Situational Training Exercise

BELOW A 5,56 mm
Steyr AUG (StG 77)

diate cartridge. There was also interest in this cartridge at Fabrique Nationale and with the Canadian Army.

With the locking system based on the Sturmgewehr design, several gas-powered rifle designs were drawn up: the EM-1, EM-2, EM-3 and the EM-4. It was the first two that made it beyond the drawing board and both of these weapons were unofficially named after the leader of each design team: the Thorpe

rifle, after Stanley Thorpe and the Janson rifle, after Stefan Janson respectively.

Both rifles were bullpup in style with the chamber and magazine lying behind the trigger and used 20-round magazines with stripper reloads as opposed to box magazines. With selective fire ability and conical optical sights for quick aiming, the new .280 round was accurate up to about 730 metres. Although the two new rifles looked similar from the outside, they were in fact made very differently on the inside. It was the EM-2 that was selected as the superior design, and although only saw brief service, was adopted by the British Army in 1951.

The Steyr AUG Austrian bullpup 5.56mm assault rifle is regarded by some as the first successful bullpup in history and was the first to become widely used. Designed in the 1960s by Steyr Mannlicher GmbH & Co KG, it went into service with the Austrian Army as the StG 77 in 1978. The rifle was very advanced for its time and was extremely reliable, accurate and light. Since its inception more than 20 other country's armed forces have adopted the rifle or its variants and it became the primary rifle of Australia as well as Austria.

The French FAMAS (Fusil d'Assaut de la Manufacture d'Armes de Saint-Ètienne) is a bullpup-type assault rifle and is the service rifle of the French military. The rifle was first developed between 1946 and 1950 and then some 40 different prototypes were designed between 1952 and 1962. Most of these were drawn up to use the NATO 7.62 x 51mm round, but the ammunition never worked with the bullpup model and these were all set aside.

Eventually, the final FAMAS design began in 1967 and the first prototype was completed in 1971. With the initial problems of production resolved the French military began issuing the rifle as standard in 1978. There were, however, many problems with the rifle including unreliability, frequent breakages of plastic components and occasional mechanism jams due to the not-so-reliable disposable magazine concept that the rifle had. By around 1994 the FAMAS G2 was then developed, which was aimed at complying with NATO standards. Although some of the French military use the G2, the FAMAS is still the primary service rifle.

With the creation of NATO in 1949, the political move towards the goal that there would eventually be commonality in the ammunition and small arms that all NATO forces would use caused many disagreements between countries as to what combination of rifles and what calibre intermediate cartridges should be used. This eventually led to the adoption of the 7.62 x 51mm NATO round from the mid-1950s.

The British, however, had a problem with this decision. All of their bullpup rifle developments (EM-2 for example) had been designed for the .280 cartridge and could not handle the more powerful NATO cartridge. This led both the British and Canadian armies to the L1A1 SLR, which was a licensed version of the FN FAL – a self-loading, selective fire rifle chambered for the NATO round and manufactured by Fabrique Nationale d'Herstal.

During the 1960s the discussions about the power of the NATO round resurfaced. Although the British had said it from the very beginning, the U.S. by that time had also come to the conclusion that the 7.62 was too powerful for the fully-automatic rifle. The Americans moved to the M16 rifle with the .223 Remington cartridge, which was ironically less powerful than the .280. By the 1970s the British could at last focus their developmental research on lighter ammunition.

Designed to fire the newly developed smaller ammunition of .190 (or 4.85mm) that offered the same recoil pattern as the American M16 ammunition, but with better ballistics and penetration, the first examples of the L64/65, an intermediate British bullpup, were available in 1972.

The small calibre round became the focus for NATO standardisation and by 1976 the testing of the different small calibre ammunitions used by different countries led to Fabrique Nationale's 5.56mm being selected.

The L64/65 evolved into the 5.56mm

SA80 (Small Arms for the 1980s) weapon family that is currently used by the British Army. The SA80 is a family of British 5.56mm selective fire, gas-operated assault rifles that were first trialled in 1976. Since 1987 the British L85 Individual weapon has been the British Armed Forces standard issue service rifle. Today the British Armed Forces use an improved version of the L85 rifle and now use the L85A2.

BELOW British Territorial Army (BTA), Private (PVT) Robert Hardingham, with the 166th Regiment, practices target shooting with an L85 Individual Weapon (IW) during a multinational exercise on the island of Benbecula, off the coast of Scotland

Chapter 17

Sniper Rifles

A sniper rifle is a rifle that can be shot with accuracy and precision from longer ranges than any other small arm is capable of. Fitted with a telescopic sight and chambered for a military centrefire cartridge, a sniper rifle is designed and made with optimum levels of accuracy as the primary objective.

Historically, the sniper rifle was an adaptation of a typical rifle, with the addition of a long-range scope. Weapons technology had advanced sufficiently so, that by the time of the American Civil War it was possible to shoot an individual from very long ranges. American confederate soldiers used the British Whitworth rifle, a single-shot muzzle-loading rifle fitted with a scope on top of the barrel; some think this to be the first ever example of an actual sniper rifle.

Telescopic sights had been experimented with dating back to the early 17th century, with the first workable telescopic rifle sight coming to fruition between 1835 and 1840. These early sights did allow a marksman[21] to observe and shoot targets at greater distances than had ever been possible before, they were however, non-adjustable to begin with, which obviously put some limitations on them.

By the outbreak of World War I the

ABOVE PSL Dragunov 7.62 mm Sniper Rifle with Telescopic sight

specially trained sniper and his rifle had become a very significant figure on the battlefield and some soldiers were given specialised training in order to be able to carry out this specific role. In Germany in particular the sniper

---

[21] *A person who is skilled in precision shooting (also known as a sharpshooter) and generally works as part of a fireteam of soldiers, as opposed to a sniper, who tends to work alone or just with other snipers.*

BELOW Red army weapons and equipment from World War II, Military Museum of Finland

rifles issued to the trained snipers were equipped with telescopic sights with some night vision capacity.

It was not until World War II, however, that the sniper (and by this time that included the she as well as the he, particularly in the Red Army) really made a marked impression on the tactics and strategies of war. Arguably more effective and ruthless (both mentally and efficiently) than some of the more obviously formidable weaponry on the battlefield such as the machine gun, the sniper had a severe and instant impact. The threat of snipers demoralised and terrified soldiers so much so that chains of command could break down on the battlefield; soldiers blatantly disregarding orders from commanding officers because of the fear of being picked off as a sniper's target.

Although we now typically regard sniping as a very accurate science, at the time, the role and skill of the sniper was very much regarded as a type of 'black art'. By the end of the war the term 'sniper' as opposed to 'marksman' was becoming a common term to describe those armed with sniper rifles, and the accuracy of these personnel had reached around 600 metres.

A U.S. Special Forces
Soldier conducts
rehearsal, training
and pre-operation
conformation on
the MK 12 sniper
rifle at sunset

Specially trained sniper regiments gradually emerged during the latter half of the 20th century and snipers and their rifles were used in Korea, Vietnam and in the Middle East. With the very difficult and demanding guerrilla warfare that armies have to now face, the role of the sniper is an integral part of modern military tactics.

Sniper rifles used conventional ammunition right up until the 1990s. More powerful ammunition was then adopted by some new designs, which not only facilitated a flatter trajectory, but also as a resulting effect of this, made the point-blank range[22] further to several hundred metres. The more powerful ammunition also meant that shooting with precision accuracy could now be carried out from even greater distances from the target. Some also redesigned the sniper rifle more substantially by adopting the 'bullpup' configuration so that whilst the all-important length of the barrel was kept in tact, the overall length of the rifle was much reduced.

The sniper rifles of today are almost

[22] *Point-blank range is the distance between a firearm and a target of a given size such that the bullet in flight is expected to strike the target without adjusting the elevation of the firearm. A firearm with a flatter trajectory will permit a farther maximum point-blank range.*

incomparable to those being used 10 years ago, let alone compared to those issued during World War II. They are also not only just used for military purposes, but are part of many law enforcement special unit weaponry. Sniper rifles designed for use in the urban environment are required to have greater accuracy than the military types, although the range of shot does not need to be so long. In view of the fact that situations that require the use of sniper rifles outside of the military is often in a built-up setting, they do not need to be quite as robust and portable as their military counterparts. Following the massacre at the 1972 Munich Summer Olympics, the West

German police were amongst the first to design a sniper rifle that would specifically meet all of their requirements. Since then, many others have followed their lead. The rifle that was developed for the West German police is the PSG1- a semi-automatic sniper rifle designed by Heckler & Koch.

The power, accuracy and durability of these modern rifles - both military and civilian - means that not only are they extremely reliable, but they retain their accuracy with repeated firing; something that was not possible before due to impact of wear and tear. In a 21st-century fighting force armoury, the sniper rifle has become one of the most deadly and efficient weapons now in use.

LEFT A 2/3 scout sniper, extracts and chambers a new round in his M40-A3 sniper rifle

BELOW A PSG1 semi-automatic sniper rifle

RIGHT Accuracy
International
G22 Arctic
7.62mm Sniper
Rifle

FAR RIGHT
Marines from
Golf Battery,
Battalion
Landing Team
aim in during a
live fire exercise

Chapter 18

Shotguns

A shotgun is generally a smooth-bore firearm that is designed to be fired from the shoulder. They come in a vast array of sizes ranging from 5.5mm bore up to 5cm bore and have also been produced using a range of firing mechanisms including break-action, bolt-action, lever-action, semi-automatic and pump-action. The cartridge that fires is either a fixed shell that fires a number of small round pellets called 'shot' or a solid projectile called a 'slug'.

The characteristic that most commonly makes a shotgun unique is concerned with the ammunition that fires shot. The shotgun cartridge (or shell in the U.S.) is a straight-walled, wide and relatively short cartridge that operates at a fairly low pressure. There are both advantages and disadvantages to shotguns. They are very effective for the close-range shooting of small and/or fast moving targets. Because of the spread-pattern of shot that is fired, the aim on the target does not have to be quite as precise than if firing with a single projectile, like the shotgun slug. Especially for static targets at close-range, the shotgun has enormous stopping power and is more powerful in this regard than nearly all handguns and many rifles. The disadvantages of shotguns lie in the fact that they have a limited range to be effective which naturally also has an

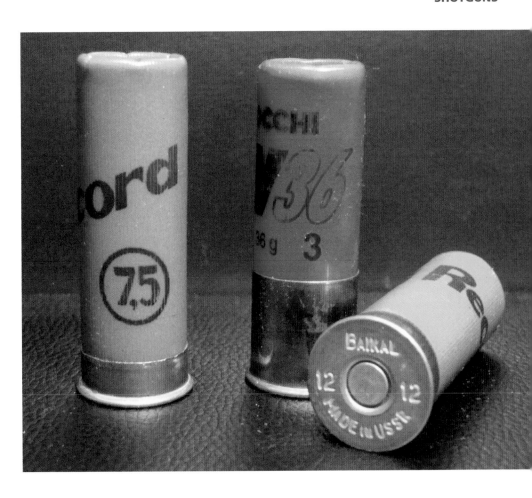

impact on the potential penetration of the shot. Although the shotgun slug has more increased penetration capabilities, the probability of hitting the target is reduced with a single projectile.

The shotgun has always been regarded as a very effective weapon when fired at close quarters. As well as being a popular sporting and hunting gun, it is used in a variety of ways in the military, in law enforcement and for personal defence. It played a valuable part during World War I and shotguns such as the Winchester Model 1897, which was a six-shot pump-action design used by American forces, became known as the 'trench sweeper'.

BELOW Winchester Model 1897, slide action open

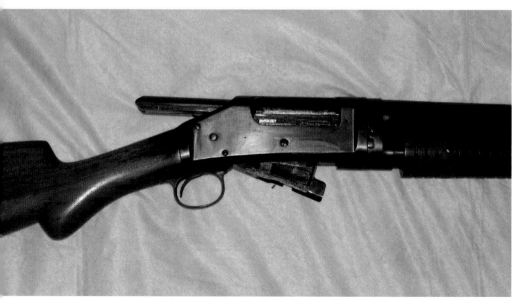

The development of shotguns put in context of the history of guns is linked to the very first smoothbore firearms, such as the muskets used by armies in the 18th century. Its direct descendant is the 'blunderbuss', which is a muzzle-loading flintlock with a short but large calibre barrel and fired with shot or similar sized projectiles.

For military purposes shotguns were mostly used and favoured by cavalry units due to its effectiveness with fast moving targets combined with its dev-

ABOVE A French Navy blunderbuss. On display at Port-Louis naval museum

astating close-range firepower. With the development of other military firearms that were more accurate over longer ranges, such as breech-loading rifled firearms, the shotgun was gradually phased out of use on the battlefield throughout the 19th century. It did, however, remain a popular weapon of defence with guards and law enforcement officers for example and with the adoption of the smaller bores and rifled barrels, the shotgun began to emerge as a separate entity.

In some cases, such as the double-barrelled shotgun, the design of such weapons changed very little following the development of the boxlock action in 1875. Other developments, however, led to the emergence of the vast array of different size, calibre and action shotguns that are now in existence.

The inventions of prolific gun designer John Moses Browning were intrinsic to the development of the modern shotgun. The Browning Model 1887 Lever Action Repeating Shotgun revolutionised shotgun design by changing the design from the common 'break open' type of loading to being able to load a new cartridge by operation of the action lever. This was then superseded in 1893 by his Model 1893 Pump Action Shotgun, which introduced the pump action to the world. In 1900 Browning then patented the world's first semi-automatic shotgun, the Browning Auto-5; this shotgun was produced until 1998, a testament to Browning's pioneering ingenuity.

Although the shotgun was not a primary weapon for the military any more, it still served its purpose in specific combat situations in World War I and, as already alluded to above, the Americans used pump action shotguns fitted with bayonets and heat shields in the Western front trenches from 1917 – these became known as 'trench guns'. During World War II, the shotgun was not used much by the military forces of Europe, but was certainly put to good use by the allied groups such as the French Resistance, the British Home Guard and the U.S. Home Security Forces. The U.S. Navy and Marine Corps on the other hand used pump-action shotguns in the humid and dirty conditions of the Pacific due to the fact that they were less likely to jam.

In conflicts since World War II the shotgun has remained in military use as a specialty weapon for tasks such as defending machine gun emplacements and in close-quarter combat. Shotguns, however, are now in use by the military far less since the development of modern pistols, rifles, carbines and submachine guns.

BELOW Browning Auto 5, barrel dismounted

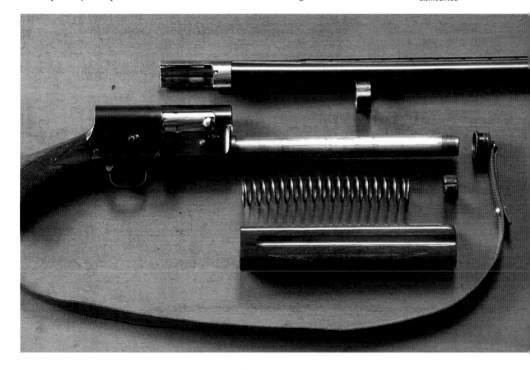

SPORTING GUNS

With regard to sporting guns specifically, by the last decade of the 19th century most of the firearm technology for these guns had been developed. As more powerful ammunition was developed thanks to the advent of new formulations of propellant, the main concerns for the on-going development of sporting guns was that of improving a gun's safety features, in addition to working on new materials to find ways of producing more economical models.

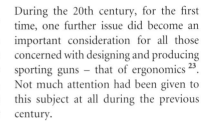

During the 20th century, for the first time, one further issue did become an important consideration for all those concerned with designing and producing sporting guns – that of ergonomics [23]. Not much attention had been given to this subject at all during the previous century.

Shotguns are very commonly used nowadays for sports such as sporting clays, trap shooting and skeet shooting. As a highly regarded, serious and skilled sport, the Olympic Games includes both skeet and trap competitions.

For hunting, again, the shotgun always has been and still is a very popular weapon throughout the world and is used for shooting birds and small game, as well as larger game such as deer. It is also particularly good for situations when it is not permitted to hunt with a rifle, for example in semi-populated areas where the range of the rifle bullet would be too dangerous to use. When this is the case, shotguns can also be fitted with rifled barrels and fired using a slug, which maximises both accuracy and performance.

[23] *The study of the interaction between individuals, machines or appliances in their environment that can affect their performance.*

Chapter 19

Glossary of terms

ACTION: the part of a firearm that loads, fires and ejects a cartridge. It includes lever-action, pump-action, bolt-action and semi-automatic. The first three are found in weapons that fire a single shot. Firearms that can shoot multiple rounds ('repeaters') include all these types of actions, but only the semi-automatic does not require manual operation between rounds.

AUTOMATIC: a firearm that will continue to load and fire whilst the trigger is pressed.

BARREL: the metal tube through which the charge is fired.

BATTERY: the state of a gun's 'action' when it is ready to fire.

BLACK POWDER: the old form of gunpowder invented over a thousand years ago and consisting of nitrate, charcoal and sulphur.

BOLT: the part of the weapon that closes and seals the 'breech'. It may also load and extract cartridges and carry the firing pin.

BOLT-ACTION: a firearm relying on a turning 'bolt' to lock its 'breech' closed.

BORE: the inside of the barrel. 'Smoothbore' weapons (typically shotguns) have no rifling. Most handguns and rifles have 'rifling'.

BREECH: the closed rear end of a gun's barrel.

BRIDLE: bridge-like supports added to lockplates to keep lateral acting parts in alignment, usually on the sear mechanisms, battery.

BULLETS: the projectile a weapon fires. They are shaped or composed differently for a variety of purposes and can be spherical, cylindro-conical (a cylinder with a cone-shaped point) or cylindro-ogival (a cylinder with a rounded point), or even hollow-pointed.

BUTT OR BUTTSTOCK: the portion of gun that is held or shouldered.

CALIBRE: the internal diameter of the barrel, usually expressed in hundredths of an inch (e.g. .22 cal) or in millimetres (e.g. 9mm).

CARTRIDGE: also called a 'round'. It con-sists of a case, primer, powder & bullet.

CENTREFIRE: the cartridge contains the primer in the centre of the base, where it can be struck by the firing pin of the action.

CHAMBER: the portion of the 'action' that holds the cartridge ready for firing.

CHARGER: a frame that holds cartridges, allowing them to be loaded into a magazine.

CHOKE: a constriction of a shotgun bore at the muzzle that determines the pattern of the fired shot.

COCK: the pivoted arm holding the match or flint, energized by a spring. When released by a holding device (sear), it is rotated forward to provide ignition to the powder by either dipping a match cord into the pan, or by causing a flint to scrape hot steel bits (sparks) from the battery into the pan. On percussion arms, the cock was referred to as the hammer, which struck a cap to ignite the powder.

CYCLE: the series of procedures necessary to fire a round and return the gun to 'battery'.

DOUBLE-ACTION: pulling the trigger

both cocks the hammer and fires the gun.

DOUBLE-BARREL: two barrels side by side or one on top of the other (usually on a shotgun).

EJECTOR: a device that throws a spent cartridge case clear after it has been extracted from the chamber.

FLASH PAN (OR PRIMING PAN): a small receptacle for priming powder, found next to the touch-hole on muzzle-loading guns.

GAS OPERATION: a firearm in which the cycle is effected by the propellant gas.

GAUGE: refers to the diameter of the barrel on a shotgun in terms of the number of lead balls the size of the bore it would take to weigh one pound (10 gauge, 12 gauge etc.).

GROOVES: the parallel spirals cut into the barrel that imparts spin to the 'bullet'.

HAMMER: a metal rod or plate that typically drives a firing pin to strike the cartridge primer to detonate the powder.

HEAD: the closed end of a cartridge case, where the primer is located.

IGNITION: the way in which powder is ignited. Old muzzle-loading weapons used flintlock or percussion caps. Modern guns use 'primers' that are 'rimfire' or 'centrefire'.

LANDS AND GROOVES: lands are the metal inside the barrel left after the spiral grooves are cut to produce the rifling.

LOCK: that part or apparatus of a firearm by which the charge is exploded; as, a matchlock, flintlock, percussion lock, etc.

MACHINE GUN: a firearm that uses 'gas' or 'recoil' to cycle its 'action' and thus give continuous fire.

MAGAZINE: the holding device for storing cartridges in a repeating firearm for loading into the chamber, usually by means of spring pressure to the 'action'.

MUZZLE: the muzzle of a firearm is the end of the barrel from which the projectile exits.

MUZZLE-LOADER: is any firearm into which the projectile and usually the propellant charge is loaded from the muzzle of the gun.

PISTOL: synonym for a handgun that does not have a revolving cylinder.

POWDER: modern gun cartridges use 'smokeless' powder that is relatively stable, of uniform quality and leaves little residue when ignited. For centuries, 'black powder' was used and was quite volatile (igniting a low temperatures or shock), was composed of irregularly sized grains, and left a heavy residue after ignition, resulting in the necessity for frequent cleaning of the bore.

PRIMER: a volatile substance that ignites when struck to detonate the powder and initiate the firing sequence. 'Rimfire' cartridges have primer inside the base, whilst 'centrefire' cartridges have primer in a hole in the middle of the base of the cartridge case.

PUMP-ACTION: a rifle or shotgun in which the handgrip can be pumped back and forth in order to eject a spent round of ammunition and chamber a fresh one.

RECOIL: the rearward movement of the barrel (or firearm) in reaction to the forward motion of the 'bullet'.

RECOIL-OPERATION: a firearm in which the 'cycle' is effected by the 'recoil' of the barrel of 'breech-block'.

REVOLVER: a handgun that has a cylinder with holes to contain the cartridges. The cylinder revolves to bring the cartridge into position to be fired. This is 'single-action' when the hammer must by cocked before the trigger can fire the gun. It is 'double-action' when pulling the trigger both cocks and fires the gun.

RIFLING: the spiral grooves cut inside a gun barrel that gives the bullet a spinning motion. The metal between the grooves is call a 'land'.

RIMFIRE: the cartridge has the primer distributed around the periphery of the base.

SAFETY: the mechanism on an action that prevents the firing of the gun.

SLOW MATCH: (or match cord) is the

GLOSSARY OF TERMS

very slow burning cord or twine fuse used by early gunpowder musketeers, artillerymen and soldiers to ignite their weapons.

SEAR: the pawl or catch in a gunlock mechanism that holds the cock or hammer at half or full cock and is released by the trigger.

SELECTIVE FIRE: a firearm that can fire both single rounds or fire automatically.

SELF-LOADING: a firearm in which the act of firing a round re-cocks it, having chambered a fresh cartridge.

SHOTGUN: a gun with a smoothbore that shoots cartridges that contain 'shot' or small metal pellets (of lead or steel) as the projectiles.

SIGHTS: the device or devices on top of a barrel that allow the gun to be aimed.

SILENCER: a device that fits over the muzzle of the barrel to muffle the sound of a gunshot; most work by baffling the escape of gases.

SINGLE-ACTION: the hammer must be manually cocked before the trigger can be pulled to fire the gun.

SMOKELESS POWDER: refers to modern gunpowder, which is really not 'powder' but flakes of nitrocellulose and other substances. Not really 'smokeless' but much less so than 'black powder'.

STOCK: a wood, metal or plastic frame that holds the 'barrel' and 'action' and allows the gun to be held firmly.

SUBMACHINE GUN: a handheld 'automatic' firearm that fires pistol-calibre rounds.

TOUCH-HOLE: a small hole through which the propellant charge of a muzzle-loading gun (or cannon) is ignited.

TRIGGER: the short lever that trips the 'sear' out of the 'bent' on the 'cock', hammer etc. to initiate the firing sequence.

ZEROING: adjusting the sights on a weapon so that the point of aim and the point of impact are the same.

The pictures in this book were provided courtesy of the following:

WIKIMEDIA COMMONS

Design & Artwork: ALEX YOUNG

Published by: DEMAND MEDIA LIMITED

Publishers: JASON FENWICK

Written by: MICHELLE BRACHET